A GEOGRAPHY OF SCOTLAND
GENERAL AND REGIONAL

A GEOGRAPHY OF
SCOTLAND

GENERAL AND REGIONAL

By

GORDON RAE, M.A.,
Principal Lecturer in Geography,
Jordanhill College of Education, Glasgow

and

CHARLES E. BROWN, M.Sc., M.Ed.,
Vice-Principal,
College of Education, Hamilton

LONDON
G. BELL AND SONS LTD
1968

Second Edition
Copyright © 1966
G. BELL AND SONS LTD
York House, Portugal Street,
London, W.C.2

First published 1959
Reprinted 1961
Second Edition 1966
Reprinted 1968

SBN 7135 0870 1

PRINTED IN GREAT BRITAIN AT
THE UNIVERSITY PRESS
ABERDEEN

PREFACE

In all but the elementary textbooks, suitable for younger pupils, the geography of Scotland has commonly been treated as the study of one region among many in the British Isles. The authors believe that a more thorough survey of Scottish geography is called for in the work of senior classes of secondary schools, and in training colleges, and that a textbook of both general and regional studies can provide a sound basis for such courses. They have endeavoured to maintain accuracy and to be up-to-date, but, since Scotland shares with other countries a rapid rate of development and change in its human geography, they recognise that complete accuracy is well nigh unattainable. Nevertheless the fuller treatment of Scotland which is presented here should correct many of the misleading generalisations and simplifications which are familiar to most geography teachers.

For the general public, Scotland should be portrayed in adequate detail as a region of distinct endowments and possibilities, both physical and human. It is hoped therefore that in this book some contribution has been made toward an understanding of Scotland's individuality and character as a modern nation.

The authors' gratitude must be recorded for the help given by many persons – in both official and private capacities – who contributed data, checked facts, and gave, in many instances, the benefit of long experience in their special spheres. They wish, furthermore, to express their appreciation of their publisher's willingness to produce a book devoted to the geography of Scotland.

G. R. and C. E. B.

January, 1959

PREFACE TO THE SECOND EDITION

The last seven years have brought a wide range of new developments in Scotland's geography, and these have merited many amendments to the earlier text, and to many of its maps and diagrams. In addition, the authors have attempted to bring the newer aspects of Scotland's economic life into sharper focus by the inclusion of a chapter devoted to such changes and trends as can be identified in a non-technical treatment of the subject. The most recent development has been the publication of the Government's *Plan for Expansion* (which reviews the prospects for the Scottish economy in the period 1965-1970) and this wide-ranging survey has been specially noted. The authors are aware of the difficulties and dangers of describing and discussing a scene of such recent and newly emerging pattern—the more so since national and international forces, both economic and political, are involved more than ever in the formation of this pattern. It is for the reader continually to amplify and revise the facts and the factors which are more clearly revealed with the passage of time.

The authors wish to express once more their gratitude for the advice and information generously provided by authorities, both professional and personal.

G. R. and C. E. B.

November, 1965

CONTENTS

PART ONE: GENERAL

PART TWO: REGIONAL

Part One: General

I · GENERAL INTRODUCTION AND PHYSICAL FEATURES

GENERAL INTRODUCTION

SCOTLAND is a small country (approx. 30,000 sq. miles) and about three-fifths the size of England. It lies on the north-west fringe of

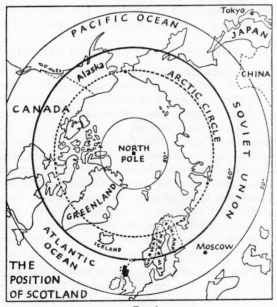

FIG. 1

Europe and forms an extension of England and Wales. The Cheviot Hills, the Solway Firth and the lower reaches of the rivers Liddel and Tweed mark the land and water boundary between the two

1

countries. On the east, Scotland is much farther away from the continent of Europe than England is. On the west, unlike England and Wales, it is fully exposed to the Atlantic Ocean and is broken up into a number of islands of which the Outer Hebrides is the main group. In the north, the Orkney Isles lie close to the mainland and the Shetland Isles more aloof. In the south-west, Ireland is only separated from Scotland by a narrow channel, 12-30 miles wide.

Scotland lies between 55° and 60° N. and is therefore not very far away from the Arctic Circle. The northern group of islands are actually closer to this latitude than to the south of England. The global map illustrates the world position of Scotland in relation to countries which are similar in latitude.

Five million people live in Scotland. The great majority of the population is concentrated in the Central Lowlands. As a whole, Scotland is not nearly so densely populated as England and Wales.

THE PHYSICAL FEATURES OF SCOTLAND

In physical appearance Scotland makes up for lack of size by great variety of landforms – highlands and lowlands, steep river courses and open haughs and carselands, deep penetrating waterways and regular coastlines, numerous inland lochs as well as a great chain of fringing islands in the west.

The formation of a rift valley through the central part of the country makes Scotland divisible naturally into a broad and familiar threefold pattern. Two series of fault-lines (neither in one continuous line) run diagonally across the country. The northern faults extend from Helensburgh to Stonehaven, the southern from Girvan to Dunbar. They mark the limits of a land subsidence which lowered the central parts of Scotland and separated the Northern Highlands from the Southern Uplands. The 1,000 foot contour line is a useful guide to the general extent of the three physical regions of Scotland.

The Northern Highlands. The Highlands form an imposing land mass occupying the northern half of the country. They are composed mostly of hard rock, igneous and metamorphic in type, and have remained upstanding and resistant to long eras of erosion by wind, water, and ice. Glen More, or The Great Glen, tear fault* is a definite division which separates the North-west Highlands from the

*A horizontal rent in the earth's surface.

Grampian mountain system. It is a natural trench, running north-east to south-west, and is occupied by long narrow lochs. West of the Great Glen, the highlands maintain a consistent height, but are broken up into very hard individual mountain blocks, like Ben

FIG. 2

Attow, Mam Soul, Ben Wyvis, and Ben More Assynt, all over 3,000 feet. Short, swift and steep hill torrents drain into the numerous sea-lochs which penetrate the whole of the coastline of north-west Scotland. In Skye, Mull and other parts, great sheets of molten lava have poured out on to the surface to form broad flat tables while at Staffa, the lava contracted as it cooled to form impressive six-sided pillars of rock. Apart from the summits of north Harris and the high land of South Uist, the Outer Hebrides compose a line of islands, low in altitude, irregular in form and pitted by innumerable lochs.

East of Glen More, the Grampian Highland block forms the highest part of the Northern Highlands and rises to an average elevation of 2,000-3,000 feet. Topographically, this area is not so much a 'chain' but rather a great elevated mass delimited by Glen More and the northern series of faults and stretching from the Moray Firth to the Firth of Clyde.

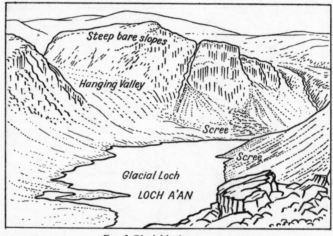

FIG. 3 Glacial loch scenery

In the latter area, the Highlands of Cowal rear up as independent summits and ridges separated by lochs that are long, penetrating culs-de-sac. Around Loch Lomond and The Trossachs are grouped several high peaks, all overlooked by the monarch-cone of Ben Lomond (3,192 feet). In the Breadalbane area (central Perthshire), the Highlands consist of high mountains (Ben More 3,843 feet, Ben Lawers 3,984 feet). They include, also, individual peaks such as Schiehallion (3,547 feet) and Ben-y-Gloe (3,671 feet), both solitary and separate summits over 3,000 feet (two of the so-called 'Munros' of Scotland).

In the north-west and north of Angus and in the adjacent parts of Perthshire and Aberdeenshire, the Grampian Highland block assumes the appearance of a chain or mountain front overlooking the north-eastern section of the Central Lowlands. Near the seaboard at Aberdeen, this highland edge disperses into low undulating terrain, but inland the mountains rise higher and higher. They reach their greatest altitude in the high and majestic massif of the Cairngorm group. Several peaks exceed 4,000 feet e.g. Braeriach, Cairngorm and Cairn Toul. Many are over 3,000 feet like Lochnagar, Ben Avon, and Beinn a Bhuird. The premier summit is Ben Macdhui whose snow-capped head rises to 4,296 feet, high above a landscape of highland tarns and torrents, of corries and scree debris.

West of the Cairngorms are the Monadhliath Mountains, a distinct range of lofty and rugged heights. They run parallel to and east of Glen More. The peaks, about 2,500 feet, are ice-worn masses which soar above a high tableland of desolate moorland. In Lochaber, further to the south-west, stands Ben Nevis, the highest mountain of Great Britain. It lies almost completely apart from the neighbouring tops and, as a stumpy tabular sentinel, it projects boldly above them, 4,406 feet high, with an imposing precipitous face to the north-east.

Throughout the entire Grampian Highland block, metamorphic, crystalline rocks are common, e.g. gneiss, schists and quartzites. These are rocks of great hardness which have been so altered by prolonged heat and pressure that their previous sedimentary state has been changed, e.g. the crystalline schists of Ben Lawers were once muds and silts. But noteworthy, also, are the great intrusions of igneous rocks, which, of molten origin, now appear at the surface as masses of granite. Grey or red in appearance, granite is most widely distributed throughout the Grampian Highland block. On account of its hardness and resistance to erosion, many of the higher parts as well as some of the familiar peaks are composed of granite.

The surface of this zone is much dissected by rivers which are longer than those to the west of Glen More. From the flanks of the highland masses descend numerous mountain torrents and purling brooks. On the Monadhliath Mountains are the headwaters of rivers Nairn, Findhorn, and Spey, all three draining into the Moray Firth. From the Cairngorms, the rivers Dee and Don, following parallel courses, cut across granite rocks to the North Sea at the city of Aberdeen. A large part of the lofty and picturesque county of Perth is drained by the river Tay and its two main tributaries, rivers Tummel and Garry. The river Tay, the longest in Scotland, 118 miles,

cuts a deep channel in its upper reaches, traverses Loch Tay, makes
an abrupt turn in its descent over the Highland edge and bends eastwards to its mouth below the city of Dundee.

The Northern Highlands of Scotland are not, however, entirely
of great altitude for three stretches of lowland run along the east
coast. In Aberdeenshire, in the extreme easterly part of Scotland,
there is the Buchan peninsula, partly of granite, much eroded and

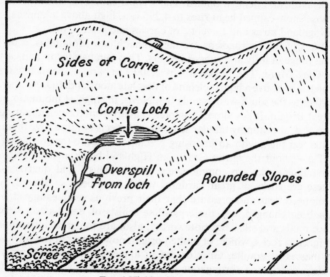

FIG. 4 Highland corrie scenery

forming undulating lowland. Similar in appearance but floored by
softer, more easily worn sandstone are the coastal margins of the
Moray Firth. In the far north, is the open triangular plain of
Caithness. Alike in its low tracts are the Orkney Isles but the Shetland Isles, although much eroded, are more akin to the North-west
Highlands in rock structure as well as in the great number of low and
penetrating sea-inlets or 'voes'.

Though ice-sheets traversed the whole length of Scotland with a
general outward flow from the high parts of the country, it is in this
zone that the best and most obvious evidence of their passage occurs.
The landforms which resulted have become familiar as characteristic

Scottish scenery. Many rivers, which are clearly misfits in their present channels, flow through broad, ice-scoured valleys or glens. Tributaries, whose valleys were subject to less erosion, may often drop steeply, by a 'hanging valley' to join the ice-deepened parent river. Some lochs now occupy scoured out basins but many, like Loch Shin and Loch Rannoch, were formed when a river valley became blocked by the accumulation of debris or moraines as the ice gradually receded. Great masses of ice-scored boulders remain on the surface while the mounds or hummocks, spread irregularly over the land, mark the final resting place of transported glacial material.

The depths of some lochs, especially those with a sea outlet, suggest that fracturing of the land followed by subsidence may be a more important cause of their formation than the work of ice alone. The Scottish sea lochs are similar to Norwegian fiords except in the height and precipitousness of their sides and in their length. Deep water sounds and kyles separate the mainland from the islands. On some, such as in the Outer Hebrides, glacial deposits and lochs cause large areas of lowland to be boggy and ill drained.

The Southern Uplands. The Southern Uplands is the name applied to the whole of the country which extends from the southern series of faults to the borders of England. They are a contrast to the Highlands because they are lower by about 1,000 feet and the gradients of the rivers are not so steep. Nor are the rocks of which they are composed so old or so resistant. But there are granite intrusions, e.g. around the imposing summit of Criffell overlooking the Solway Firth as well as in the higher parts of Kirkcudbright. The entire area was likewise traversed by ice-sheets which in their passage rounded off the hills and left typical glacial deposits. There are fewer lochs in this part of Scotland and they are smaller and less elongated. The whole region forms a plateau of moderate height, with grassy moorlands and broken by many rivers flowing through holms or rich fertile valleys.

In the eastern section, the northern slopes of the Cheviot Hills and the southern faces of the Lammermuir and Moorfoot Hills enclose the basin of the river Tweed. It flows in an easterly direction to its silted estuary at Berwick in Northumberland and is the recipient of the waters of many left and right bank tributaries like the Gala Water and the rivers Ettrick and Teviot.

An elevated plateau in the extreme west of the Tweed Basin forms the watershed of three important rivers: the river Tweed draining eastwards to the North Sea; the river Clyde descending northwards to the Central Lowlands; and the river Annan dropping southwards.

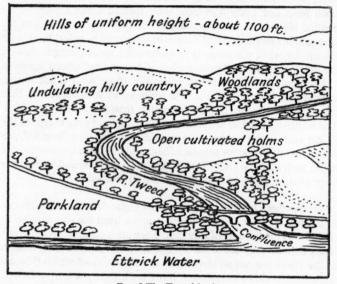

FIG. 5 The Tweed basin

This river, as well as rivers Nith and Esk, occupy picturesque dales and follow parallel courses to the Solway Firth.

In the western section, high rolling uplands and bare granite moors tilt southwards to merge into the Galloway lowlands which skirt the length of the Solway Firth. The Rhinns and the Machers of Wigtown form southward-facing lowland remnants of a submerged coast while Loch Ryan is a sheltered and narrow sea-loch cul-de-sac facing north.

The Central Lowlands. Approximately 120 miles from south-west to north-east and 50 miles broad, this region is delimited on the north and south by the great lines of faults. Only in its relation to the country's other regions may it be regarded as a lowland for there are some distinct hill groups. The fault lines mark it off as a rift valley, formed as a result of the subsidence of the area between these faults, but only in this sense can it be termed a valley. The junction of the Central Lowlands and the Highlands is well marked at the north eastern end of the rift valley because of the presence of Strathmore but there is no such counterpart along the southern fault line.

Along the front of the Highland edge, from the vicinity of Loch Lomond to the Mearns in Kincardine is a fairly continuous stretch of undulating territory, traversed by the rivers Forth and Tay. Between the Highland edge and the Sidlaw Hills is the broad and open plain of Strathmore.

A line of uplands of volcanic origin extends from Angus to Dunbartonshire and is broken into individual ranges by the main rivers. The river Tay separates the Sidlaw Hills from the Ochil Hills which in turn are severed by the river Forth from the Campsie Fells and Kilpatrick Hills. On the south side of the river Clyde, volcanic hills reappear often as flat topped uplands and are named collectively the Renfrew Heights. In Fife, broken and lower extensions of similar uplands take the place of distinct ranges.

In the southern section of central Scotland and contiguous with the Southern Uplands is a belt of high ground from East Lothian to Ayrshire. The Lammermuir, Moorfoot and Pentland Hills stand out as definite hill ranges. On either side of the middle Clyde valley a foreland of low moors protrudes northwards, of sufficient altitude to mark off areas of plain. The Ayrshire plain, possessing a westerly drainage system, is almost entirely encircled by hills. The river Clyde, whose headwaters are on the borders of Dumfriesshire, descends gradually from the Southern Uplands, sweeps round the prominent volcanic mass of Tinto and drops abruptly over the falls of Bonnington, Corra Linn, and Stonebyres. It then flows through a valley which expands into a broad plain in the vicinity of Glasgow. The lower Clyde is a commercial highway which becomes a deep and widening firth beyond Gourock. Between the rivers Clyde and Forth a belt of lowland, about 30 miles long, forms a narrow and natural corridor which gives access to the carselands skirting the Firth of Forth.

In addition to volcanic ranges, many individual stumps of similar origin remain upstanding in the Central Lowlands while the surrounding rocks have been reduced. Dundee Law, the Castle Rocks of Stirling and Edinburgh, Dumbarton Rock, and Neilston Pad are good examples.

The passage of ice-sheets accounts for the general appearance of the surface of this part of Scotland, for not only did they scour the surface to a smooth contour but they also left many typical signs of

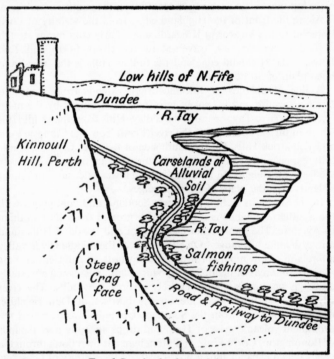

FIG. 6 Carselands of central Scotland

their passage, e.g. the stretches of boulder clay spread over Strathmore, the numerous drumlins or rounded hills in the city of Glasgow and the debris now marking the descent from the Castle Rock of Edinburgh. Following the ice invasion, the land surface experienced gradual elevations which are now indicated by the low raised beaches, e.g. in Renfrewshire and Angus and by the level carselands along the firths of Clyde, Forth and Tay.

II · CLIMATE

THE climate of Scotland is greatly influenced by its position on the extreme north-west margin of the land mass of Europe. The seas which enclose Scotland on three sides and send their waters far up the firths are relatively warm, for they are part of the North Atlantic Drift composed of water derived from the Gulf of Mexico. In general, too, they are cooler than the land in summer and warmer in winter and thus exert a great influence over the air-streams which pass across Scotland.

Temperature. Figs. 7 and 8 show the isotherms for January and July. They show that, during the entire year, there is not a great variation in temperature throughout the country. For its latitude, too, Scotland does not experience those extremes of temperature in summer and winter met with at places set in continental land masses.

Place	Latitude	January	July	Annual Range
Fort William	56° 48′ N.	39° F.	57° F.	18° F.
Dundee	56° 28′ N.	37° F.	58° F.	21° F.
Winnipeg	49° 55′ N.	−4° F.	66° F.	70° F.
Kasan (U.S.S.R.)	55° 50′ N.	7° F.	68° F.	61° F.

The isotherms in winter run north-south, particularly in the west. Their trend suggests that the chief source of warmth is the adjacent Atlantic Ocean over which constant airstreams or prevailing westerlies move towards the land. The western coasts including the fringe of islands near and off the mainland are mildest in winter and experience temperatures around 40°. There is not a very great difference, however, between the west and east coasts. Average temperatures at Stornoway and Aberdeen are not dissimilar, and in the Central Lowlands a belt of warmth exists in the Clyde-Forth corridor. Less influenced by the sea are the higher inland parts in the northern half of Scotland.

In the summer time, the 58° and 59° isotherms enclose the centre of the country, but in the north and in the south, they run roughly east – west and indicate that latitude is also an important influence

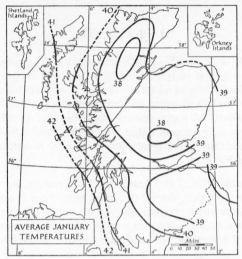

FIG. 7

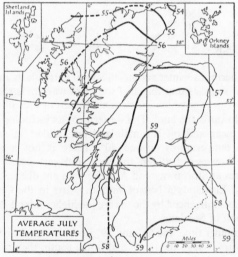

FIG. 8

at this season as well as the relative heating and cooling of the land and sea. The south of Scotland around the Solway Firth enjoys moderately high temperatures and there is a gradual decrease northwards with no abrupt regional changes. The Shetland Isles experience average temperatures 5° lower than Galloway.

In no part of the country do the isotherms show a very large annual range. It varies from 15° in the west to 19° in the east. It is important to remember, however, that these isotherm maps show temperatures which have been 'reduced to sea-level', a procedure which enables comparisons to be made without having to allow for altitude. The drops in temperatures, occasioned by altitude, are

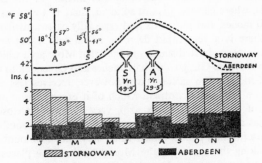

FIG. 9 Climatic comparisons between Aberdeen and Stornoway – temperature and rainfall

usually estimated at 1° F. fall for a rise of 300 feet. The higher parts of Scotland do, therefore, experience temperatures which are much lower than those shown. Similar isotherm maps for other months illustrate another noteworthy point. From April to November, the whole of Scotland experiences average temperatures above 41° F., a figure which is about the limit of plant growth. This is an important feature but unless it is understood that the isotherm maps refer to sea-level conditions, a misconception may easily be made.

The rise and fall of temperature throughout the year in Scotland is normal, with January and July the accepted coldest and warmest months. Of interest, too, is the duration of sunshine because of the direct connection between sunshine and human activities such as agriculture and catering for visitors. Scotland, as a whole, has an average duration of sunshine of 3-4 hours per day. The islands of Coll and Tiree have the highest average of 4 hours sunshine per day. Along the east, west and south coastal parts there are 3·5 hours. Sunshine is least in the areas which are highest and so prone to cloudiness. There is also a smaller amount of sunshine in the industrial sections of the Forth-Clyde corridor in which, especially in cold winter spells, fog may persist at ground level.

Rainfall. Fig. 10 shows the distribution and annual amounts of rain over the country. The western part of Scotland receives most rain. The increase in height and rainfall is clear especially in Inverness-shire, Argyll, and Ross and Cromarty in all of which are lofty areas with a very high total of 80-100 inches. In the Southern Uplands, where elevation is not so great, there is a copious rainfall of 50-60 inches. But outwards and especially eastwards from these areas, there is a very rapid decrease in rainfall. There are sharp variations over short distances in the Glen More area while about 20 miles separate Glasgow with 37 inches and Greenock to the west with 62 inches. The eastern part, however, receives less rain and provides a very good contrast. Much of it experiences a moderate rainfall of 30-40 inches but a strip, very narrow and close to the coast, has a low record of less than 30 inches. In the south, nearly the entire lowland of the Tweed valley has similar amounts; to the north, along the shores of the Moray Firth, some places have a precarious maximum of 25 inches. Worth observation, also, is the area of lighter rainfall in the lowlands of western Ayrshire; the correspondence of isohyets and elevations in the Forth, Tay, and Tweed valleys; and the greater amount of rainfall in the Shetland Isles compared to the Orkney Isles which is more akin to the eastern mainland.

Except in the western areas where there are large seasonal differences, the fall of rain does not vary very much from month to month. Most places experience more rain in the second half of the year while a spell of fair weather is very common between April and June. In parts, e.g. in Glasgow and Edinburgh, it is not uncommon to find a slight maximum in July and/or August, a feature which resembles the rainfall regime of a large continent but which is possibly occasioned by a convection storm precipitating a heavy downpour of rain.

Falls of snow start on high ground at least in the last two months of the year. They are not normally very great but reach their heaviest in the early months of the year. Snow accumulates on

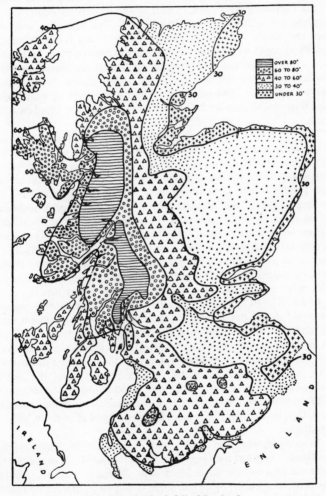

FIG. 10 Annual rainfall of Scotland

sunless slopes, in corries and rock depressions, so that some parts of the Highlands may not be completely clear of snow until May.

The rainfall in Scotland is due, in part, to the influence of relief on the prevailing winds and in part to the passage of depressions. Scotland lies within the westerly wind belt. The westerlies, coming over the North Atlantic Drift, are warmed and reach Scotland heavily charged with water vapour. As the highest parts lie to the west side of Scotland, the westerly airstreams are forced to rise. Cooling ensues, condensation of the water vapour follows and rain (often called relief rain) falls. The higher parts of west Scotland thus receive heavier falls than the lower and the more eastern parts.

The westerly winds are closely associated with the passage of 'depressions' across or very near to Scotland. They take their rise, very often, not far distant in the North Atlantic Ocean where warm airstreams of equatorial origin mingle with cold air from polar areas. The lighter, warm air is raised aloft over the colder air. There is cooling of the air and condensation of the water vapour and rain (often called cyclonic rain) falls. These are not static disturbances but move frequently towards Scotland, often as a series. They vary in direction and speed of travel, in intensity, and in duration. They may occur at any time of the year but affect Scotland mostly in the winter months. Then their passage is marked by unsettled conditions with relative mildness and much cloudy or rainy weather.

In addition to the variable nature of the depressions themselves, the rapid day-to-day changes in the weather – so noticeable a trait in Scotland – arise mainly from the conflict between the depressions or low pressure systems of the North Atlantic and the low (summer) and high (winter) pressure conditions over the continent of Europe. This is most obvious in winter. The rainy weather of the North Atlantic depression may give way, quickly, to the continental high pressure spell, dry, clear, and frosty and, with similar suddenness, this, in turn, may be broken by another period of rainy, muggy conditions.

In summer, when the low pressure of the Continent extends over Scotland, a very hot spell may oust the rainy conditions of the North Atlantic depressions. In a lesser way, Scotland may also be influenced, in summer, by an indraught of hot air from a high pressure belt around the Azores.

Summary of the Climatic characteristics of Scotland
An equable climate – the West Maritime Type:

1. Winter warmth (for its latitude), particularly in the west.
2. Small seasonal variations in temperatures; ice-free conditions.
3. Much rain in the west; west wind prevailing in most parts.
4. Great variability.

The significance of climate. The most important and general effect which climate has on Scottish activities is that ice-free conditions prevail throughout the entire year. The arrival and departure of passenger vessels proceeds uninterrupted. There is no winter freeze-up to suspend the import and export trade, the life-blood of the country. Coastwise traffic goes on at all times of the year – Ayrshire coal to Ireland, Angus seed potatoes to ports around The Wash, landing of white fish by Scottish trawlers at their home ports. While it is true that, for fully five months, sea communications cease between Clydeside and the ice-bound St. Lawrence ports, airlinks are maintained all the year round between North America and Prestwick, the Ayrshire airport, which enjoys far greater freedom from winter fogs than any other in Great Britain.

The very high amounts of rainfall are most valuable. Many lochs are natural storages of drinking water for urban and rural communities. Loch Katrine, source of the major part of Glasgow's water supply, is a striking example, but a glance at a large scale map will endorse the value of even the smaller lochs in this respect. The utilisation of Scotland's water resources in the generation of hydro-electricity depends entirely upon the copious (but not overabundant) rainfall which is collected from large catchment areas into natural and artificial reservoirs both in the Highlands and in the Southern Uplands.

A great number and variety of industries rely on local or easily accessible water which is vital in the brewing, chemical, paper, textile and other industries. There can never be enough water in Scotland to meet the needs of everyone, but the nature lover and the fisherman may despair at the disturbance to wild life and the pollution of the rivers resulting from the increasing energies of the industrialist.

Climate is the farmers' concern. Temperatures which fall below

42° F. in winter may render it difficult to maintain a growing sward for feeding stock out-of-doors while great elevation and/or lack of sunshine may be a discouragement to the growth and harvest of crops as well as a hazard in the care of animals in winter. Frost can be as great an inconvenience in the autumn lifting of root crops as can its damage to fruit blossom be a grave loss in the spring.

	Lerwick		Renfrew		Ft. William		Dumfries		Edinburgh	
	Temp.	Rain	Temp.	Rain	Temp.	Rain	Temp.	Rain	Temp.	Rain
Jan.	38·2° F.	4·5″	38·4° F.	4·7″	38·9° F.	9·8″	37·6° F.	3·9″	37·4° F.	2·4″
Feb.	37·9° F.	3·3″	39·3° F.	3·2″	39·7° F.	7·1″	38·5° F.	2·3″	38·8° F.	1·7″
March	39·0° F.	3·1″	41·9° F.	2·5″	42·4° F.	5·0″	41·6° F.	2·3″	41·7° F.	1·6″
April	41·5° F.	2·7″	45·4° F.	2·3″	45·8° F.	4·7″	45·2° F.	2·0″	45·9° F.	1·6″
May	45·6° F.	2·2″	50·4° F.	2·6″	50·7° F.	3·9″	51·0° F.	2·3″	50·5° F.	2·2″
June	49·5° F.	2·1″	55·6° F.	2·4″	55·3° F.	4·4″	56·0° F.	2·5″	56·1° F.	1·9″
July	53·5° F.	2·5″	58·8° F.	3·1″	57·7° F.	5·3″	59·0° F.	3·4″	59·4° F.	2·8″
Aug.	53·5° F.	2·8″	58·0° F.	3·3″	57·8° F.	5·9″	58·4° F.	3·9″	58·5° F.	3·0″
Sept.	50·6° F.	3·7″	54·0° F.	3·6″	54·2° F.	6·9″	54·4° F.	3·3″	55·0° F.	2·5″
Oct.	45·9° F.	4·4″	48·4° F.	4·7″	48·8° F.	9·1″	48·3° F.	3·9″	49·3° F.	2·8″
Nov.	42·0° F.	4·6″	42·0° F.	4.1″	43·2° F.	7·7″	41·9° F.	3·4″	43·0° F.	2·4″
Dec.	39·8° F.	4·4″	39·6° F.	4·2″	40·3° F.	8·6″	38·7° F.	3·5″	39·7° F.	2·1″

	Range	Total	Range	Total	Range	Total	Range	Total	Range	Total
Year	15·3° F.	40·3″	20·4° F.	40·7″	18·9° F.	78·4″	21·4° F.	36·7″	20·0° F.	26·7″

Source of above figures: *The New Atlas of Great Britain*. O.U.P. and *Atlas of Edinburgh* Geographical Association, Edinburgh Branch.

In other respects, not less important, it is far from easy to belittle the significance of the Scottish climate. Not only heavy but continuous rain allied to hill mist reduces much of the appeal of Scottish scenery to the visitor. For the ski-ing enthusiast, there are some fine locations in the Highlands although the uncertainty of the snow cover restricts the complete development of such winter sports in Scotland.

III · MANPOWER

THE 'working population' of Scotland is less than half the total population (2¼ million in civil employment, out of 5 million people), for this term is used to include only those working in industry, commerce and administration or other 'service' workers. It is this 'working' population which is geographically important since it forms the links between 'place' and 'people'.

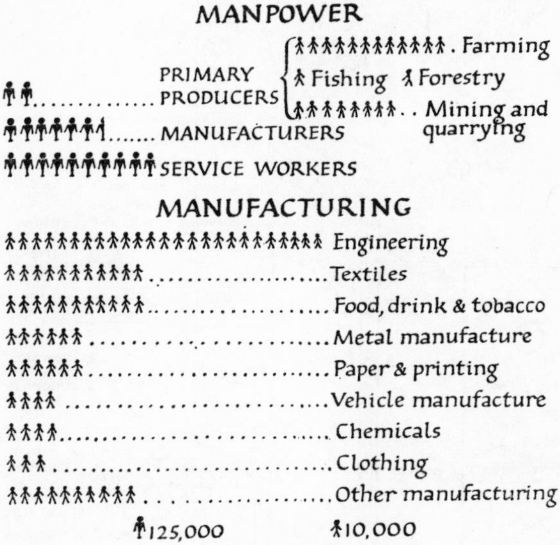

MANPOWER

PRIMARY PRODUCERS — Farming, Fishing, Forestry, Mining and quarrying

MANUFACTURERS

SERVICE WORKERS

MANUFACTURING

Engineering

Textiles

Food, drink & tobacco

Metal manufacture

Paper & printing

Vehicle manufacture

Chemicals

Clothing

Other manufacturing

125,000   10,000

Fig. 11

Rather less than half of the Scottish working population is employed in industries which are productive, i.e. on farms, on the sea, in mines, and in factories. The others work in shops and offices, on buses and trains, on building and on all other services which are necessary for life today. Thus, when all these 'non-producers' are allowed for, only a little over one million people remain as the industrial workers of Scotland; these provide the food, the fuel, the

19

timber and all the manufactured goods which Scotland has for home use and for export.

Four-fifths of these industrial workers are engaged in manufacture, including the repair and maintenance of manufactured goods. The other fifth work as primary producers, gaining the

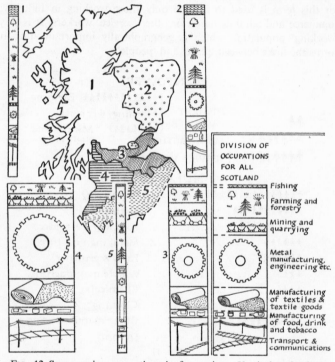

DIVISION OF OCCUPATIONS FOR ALL SCOTLAND

Fishing

Farming and forestry

Mining and quarrying

Metal manufacturing, engineering etc.

Manufacturing of textiles & textile goods

Manufacturing of food, drink and tobacco

Transport & communications

FIG. 12 Seven major occupations in five regions. Vertical scale shows the relative importance of the occupations; areas represent actual numbers employed.

natural products of land and sea. Two kinds of 'primary' production – farming and mining – appear all important in the diagram of 'Manpower' (Fig. 11). Fishing, which employs 11,000, and forestry with 7,000 workers are not unimportant, however, for again account must be taken of the geographical significance of industries which link human activities with the land and the sea. (The fishing industry has an importance too as an indirect employer: twice as many people are engaged in ancillary occupations such as curing as in fishing itself.)

Nevertheless Scotland is a country of large manufacturing industries, with a great concentration of effort on relatively few products. This concentration is largely on heavy industry, e.g. steel, engineering, and shipbuilding; but newer, lighter industries of a varied nature began with the establishment of Industrial Estates before the war. These will be referred to in more detail later.

Some regional variations are shown in the diagrams of seven major occupations, on page 20. In the crofting counties, and in the south (regions 1 and 5 respectively) these seven occupations account for half the working population; in the Central Lowlands, both east and west (regions 3 and 4), they account for a little over a third of the total, a difference which reflects the greater diversity of industry in the urban areas. The north-east region (2) has quite naturally an intermediate position in this respect. While both sides of the Central Lowlands show great concentration on manufacturing, compared with primary industries, the west is much more biased in this direction, the east having twice as high a proportion of farmers and miners.

But manufacturing is important in every region; even in the crofting counties a fifth of the workers in these seven occupations are employed in the 'metal', 'textile', and 'food' groups. These three have been shown, from among the many other manufacturing trades, because of their widespread occurrence and geographical importance. Metal-making and engineering in the west Central Lowlands; mining and quarrying in the east Central Lowlands; textiles and clothing in the south; farming and fishing in the north; these are specialisations which are only relative to the other regions. For the other two occupations, the food and transport groups, one may note how important they are in all regions.

The concentration of industrial workers in the Central Lowlands is in keeping with the general distribution of population. In fact, two-fifths of those employed in Scotland work in the four cities, and a further quarter in four counties – Lanark, Renfrew, Ayr, and Fife – making a concentration of over two-thirds of Scotland's labour force in the 'four city, four county' pattern.

Some Scottish industries employ many men but few women. This is especially true of agriculture, forestry and fishing in the rural and coastal areas, and of mining and 'heavy' industry in the Central Lowlands. While there are twice as many men as women employed

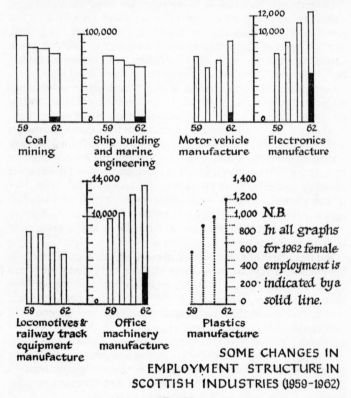

SOME CHANGES IN EMPLOYMENT STRUCTURE IN SCOTTISH INDUSTRIES (1959–1962)

FIG. 13

in all Scottish industries, there are almost seven times as many in agriculture, forestry, and fishing; ten times as many in metal manufacture; seventeen times as many in shipbuilding; and forty times as many in mining and quarrying. The major employment of women and girls is in the distributive trades (especially in shops) but among the manufacturing industries textiles is outstanding, and here the general proportion is reversed: almost twice as many women are employed as men. Second in importance for female labour are the food, drink, and tobacco industries.

More detail of Scotland's industrial structure is given in the following chapters where it is shown that many changes are taking place in the pattern of employment. While the traditionally important heavy manufacturing industries remain at the core of Scotland's economy, some of them are losing ground and newer sources of more varied employment arise, e.g. in the electronics and motor-car industries. The electronics and office machinery factories offer work to both men and women, and even the manufacture of motor vehicles is better in this respect than the manufacture of locomotives or ships. The diagrams above show some of these variations, but one should note the differences in scale and how small is the total number employed in plastics.

IV · FARMING

THE farming activities of Scotland, throughout this century, have been made possible as a result of a series of agricultural improvements which began two centuries ago. Some of the striking developments have been the enclosure of land into self-contained farms, nowadays mostly owner-occupied, the improvement of the breeds of livestock, the practice of liming and underground drainage, the culture of root crops like the potato and the turnip, the improvement of grasslands, the establishment of regular crop rotations, the use of artificial fertilisers and, of more recent date, the invention of many types of mechanical contrivances. In converting Scotland from a rude and backward condition, all these measures have made their contribution. Not least have been the very valuable achievements of agricultural colleges at Glasgow, Edinburgh, Aberdeen and elsewhere, each of which exists to conduct research, to give a scientific education to farmers-to-be and to provide expert knowledge on farming matters.

Livestock and fodder crops, and the use of improved artificial feeding stuffs, are fundamental in Scottish farming. Even the 'arable' farm, enjoying a growing season of six months, has long been concerned with the fattening of cattle and sheep. This concern with animals provides an element of unity, linking the impoverished crofter at one end of the scale, with the more fortunate Lothian farmer at the other. Yet there is great variety; the higher areas are more extensively farmed for hill sheep; lower down, in the valleys, young animals are reared, both cattle and sheep; on the carselands and coastal plains, cropping, fattening, and dairy farming are most important.

The three zones and their east-west variations stand out very clearly. The Highlands and Islands have a wide, central core of hill-sheep farming; this includes many grouse moors and deer 'forests' (treeless tracts of heather and coarse grass) and it is interrupted by crofting clachans and by true forests. The lower coastal land of the west, especially in the islands, is capable of stock rearing, i.e. young cattle and sheep can be supported in less extensive pasturage and the crofts are more concentrated. To the east, the lower hills and glens (notably Strath Spey) are also stock-rearing lands. As an

24

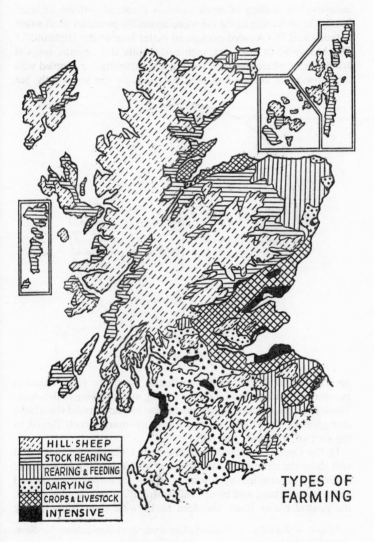

HILL SHEEP
STOCK REARING
REARING & FEEDING
DAIRYING
CROPS & LIVESTOCK
INTENSIVE

TYPES OF FARMING

Fig. 14

3

industry, the rearing of stock remains a special interest of smal family farms 'strung along the more accessible glens, on wind-swept uplands and in favoured pockets of better land in the Highlands'.* The Moray Firth lowlands, with better soils and climate, support arable farms where livestock rearing and fattening are coupled with the growing of cereals and seed potatoes. In the less kindly but

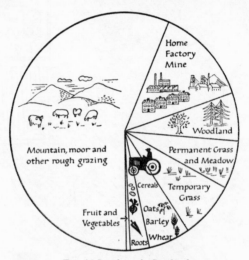

FIG. 15 Land use in Scotland

nevertheless fertile soils of the north-east, much the same system is pursued but the emphasis is on the rearing and fattening of livestock. These two farming types of the north-east lowlands avoid the straths and glens of the Highlands and are much more closely linked to the east of Scotland, generally.

In the Central Lowlands and Southern Uplands, the north and east show the strongest development of arable farming in Scotland. Although interrupted by lowlands where fattening of cattle and sheep is important, and by uplands where hill-sheep farming recurs, the coastal plains from Aberdeen to Berwick show crops taking

Types of Farming in Scotland (Department of Agriculture for Scotland) H.M.S.O., 1952.

first place in farming interests. To the south and west of Scotland, dairying is especially prevalent in the lowland farms. Here the northern fault-line marks a clear cleavage between the Highland hill-sheep farms and the Lowland dairy farms. In the counties south of it, including the fringing lowlands of Bute and Argyll, dairying occupies all but the higher sheep lands. Stock rearing and fattening is of much less interest in these areas and it is noteworthy that, in Scotland as a whole, dairy farms take first place numerically and in value of output. The contrast of east and west in the lowlands of Scotland is one of grass management and of crops for fodder and for sale. To the west, permanent pasture is much more important than elsewhere in Scotland; to the east, crops and rotation grass take up most of the land. The contrast between permanent pasture for dairy cattle in the west and arable farming in the east is most clearly seen in Ayrshire and Fife. Permanent pasture is almost a half of the area under crops and grass in Ayrshire. In Fife it is only one seventh. This contrast is emphasised by the fact that crops for sale off the farm are generally unimportant in the west but are of great importance in the east.

The hill-sheep farms form a cross-pattern, linking east and west in southern Scotland, following the lines of volcanic hills in the Central Lowlands and the broader hill areas of the Southern Uplands. Although smaller as an area than the Highland sheep farms (the individual farms are smaller too), they are more densely stocked because the soil is much more fertile. The south-west of Scotland has nearly 33 per cent of the hill-sheep farms of Scotland; the Highlands nearly 40 per cent. The sheep farms of the south-east, though fewer in number, are more highly stocked than those in other regions.

Another cross-thread running through the arable and dairy lands of central Scotland is a tendency to specialise in crops such as fruit and vegetables and in livestock such as poultry and pigs. These farming activities are more intensive in methods, more clearly related than others to nearness of markets and more dependent on good soils and climate.

THE LIVESTOCK OF SCOTLAND

Sheep. As befitting a mountainous and hilly country, Scotland is famed for its sheep. No other class of animal, providing meat, skins and fibre, makes such good use of the rough vegetation of the hills as the two familiar breeds of Scottish sheep, the Blackface and the Cheviot.

About $3\frac{3}{4}$ million of Scotland's $8\frac{1}{2}$ million sheep are found in the counties of the southern and south-western uplands. Of the two breeds, the hardy, horned, black or speckled faced Blackface with its long coat of coarse wool, used largely for carpet making, is the more numerous. It is the sheep of the heather as opposed to the more grass covered hills where the Cheviots predominate. This breed is white faced and hornless. Their wool, which is finer in texture, has long been used in the textile industry of the Tweed valley although the mills now make use of woollen fibres from many distant sheep-lands. Of recent years, Cheviots have been divided into two distinct types largely as a result of the different environmental conditions of the extreme north and south of Scotland. Aptly enough, they are termed the north country and the south country Cheviot, the former having a longer body, longer legs and non-erect ears.

Both Cheviots and Blackfaces yield excellent mutton. The ewes of both breeds, after producing three or four crops of lambs on the hills, are purchased by farmers whose arable lands skirt the hillsides. On these marginal-land farms, they are mated with rams of the Border-Leicester – another Scottish breed – to produce the well known Crosses or Halfbreeds. Both are noted for their excellent mutton qualities and for their prolificacy as ewes. Half-bred females are in great demand for breeding, not only on the low ground arable stock-raising farms in the Lowlands but also in counties as far south as Kent. They are usually crossed with rams of the English Down breeds.

Thus the Scottish breeds of sheep play a most important part in the output of Scottish agriculture. Not only do they produce wool and mutton from the hill lands, thus releasing valuable land for the production of cereals, potatoes, and sugar beet, but they also give to the low ground farmers the class of breeding sheep which they require.

Shepherding, in Scotland, is by no means an easy pursuit. There is a constant and anxious struggle with a fickle climate. Majestic and colourful in its grandeur, highland and upland moorland may turn, almost without warning, into expanses of grim and hazardous terrain, windswept, shrouded in mist and rain or deep in wreaths of snow. There is scant opportunity for leisure at any time of the year.

The lambing months in Scotland extend through March and April. Much lambing takes place on the open hill but many shepherds erect straw windbreaks to protect the young animals in their early days. Dipping, i.e. immersing sheep in water containing disinfectant,

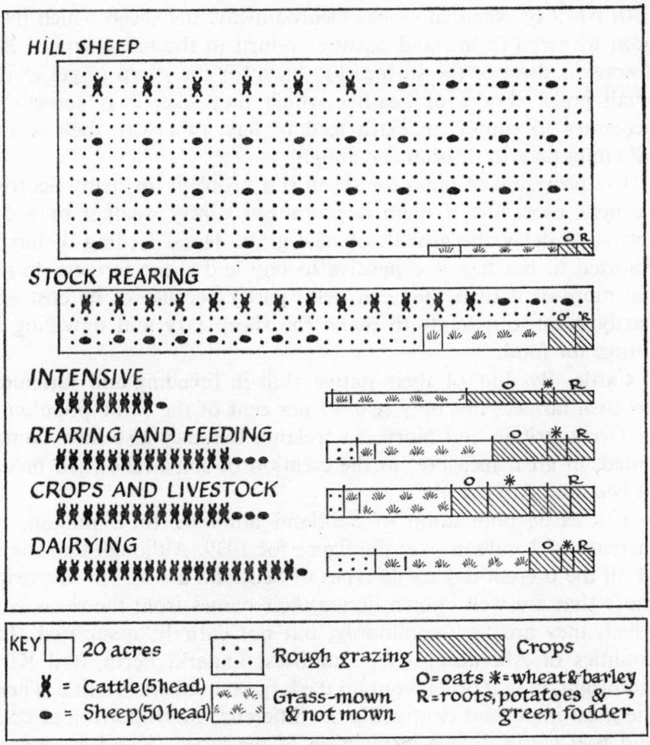

FIG. 16 Land use and stock: farm averages

takes place in summer and in winter months but some Scottish shepherds like their flocks to undergo more than the usual dippings for then there is more likelihood of their animals being free of parasites which cause disease, irritate the skin or injure the wool clip. June is the month of shearing throughout most of Scotland and, in late summer, the best female lambs are frequently taken off the hill pastures and sent for winter feeding to lowland grazings particularly along the eastern coastlands. The other lambs, not required for breeding, and the older ewes, 5-6 years of age, are despatched to the autumn sheep sales which take place all over Scotland from Tongue to Dumfries.

In April or when snow has cleared away, the sheep which have been wintered in lowland pastures return to the hill grazings. But if snow is deep or the surface too hard for the sheep to get at the small green shoots of heather which they like, it is sometimes necessary to supply an extra feed of hay, otherwise their winter fattening may have been for nought.

The provision of grass for sheep is a problem for many Scottish farmers, especially if there is prolonged wintry weather or a dry spring to delay the growth of new grass. Hand feeding of hay is resorted to but hay is expensive to buy and sheep farmers do not use more of it than they can help, partly because of its cost and partly because it tends to make the sheep lazy and unwilling to forage for food.

Cattle. By dint of their native skill in breeding and fattening, Scottish farmers not only rear 17 per cent of the cattle population of Great Britain and Northern Ireland, but they also have contributed, in great measure, to the creation of some renowned breeds of beef and dairy cattle.

The cattle population of Scotland amounts to 2 million, an increase of ¾ million over the figure for 1939. Although the origins of all the present day cattle types of Scotland are lost in obscurity, those that are well known derive their names from the areas with which they are now commonly, but not entirely, associated. The counties of Aberdeen, Ayr, Dumfries, Lanark, Perth, and Kirkcudbright, in that order, contain the largest numbers of cattle. There, the most important contrast is the difference in proportion of dairy and beef cattle. In the production of the latter, Aberdeen is most outstanding. In this county, along with Banff, Moray, Kincardine, Angus, and Perth, the Aberdeen-Angus cattle type and its crosses predominate. Such cattle are black, polled or hornless, and yield beef of the very best quality. In other parts of northern Scotland, are found the picturesque Highland cattle, whose shaggy tan-coloured hide and outspread horns are easy to distinguish. They are strong enough to endure the exposed and inclement conditions of their highland home but, although their meat is of high quality, they have not been sent abroad in such large numbers as the other types.

The daily supplies of fresh milk for the urban centres of Central Scotland come mostly from Ayrshire, Lanarkshire and the Solway counties. There the familiar animals are the Ayrshire and Galloway types. Originally evolved in the Cunningham part of the county, the Ayrshire breed has erect horns, is brown and white in colour and has become one of the best producers of milk in quality as well as in quantity.

The Galloway cattle, most common in the Solway regions, are black or brown-black, hornless and not unlike the Aberdeen-Angus in appearance. They are hardy animals and, although slower to mature than the Aberdeen-Angus, they fatten well and are most acceptable in the meat market. The Belted Galloway, so called on account of the white band encircling the body, thrives well on the rich pastures of the south and is acknowledged as a generous milk producer. The Shorthorn has its origin in Durham but the high reputation of the breed, as a dairy or beef type, can be traced to last century when, by careful selection and perseverance, Scottish breeders were successful in producing a very fine beef strain. Red, white, and roan in appearance, Shorthorns are popular in many parts of Scotland, mostly as beef cattle. They have been successfully cross-bred, e.g. a Galloway and Shorthorn cross gives an exceedingly good meat producer.

An index of the repute which Scottish pedigree cattle have acquired is evident in the interest of home and overseas buyers. Every year at Perth, at the pure-breed sales of Aberdeen-Angus and Shorthorns, vast sums are paid for breeding animals to go to North and South America, Australia, New Zealand and elsewhere. Ayrshires are largely purchased by English buyers, but many also go abroad. That Scotland is foremost in the production of high grade cattle is not an exaggerated assertion.

Yet the limit of progress and resourcefulness has not been reached. Once more, grass is the major consideration. There is a need for greater conservation of grass in the field and as silage to supplement the use of imported cattle cake. The provision of shelter belts for beasts in winter to make possible all-the-year-round outdoor feeding is a feature which, already in existence in a few places, may prove to be more than a novelty in cattle rearing in Scotland.

CEREALS

Wheat. Because temperatures are not high enough and rainfall is too great, most parts of Scotland are unsuitable for the successful cultivation of wheat. Wheat fields can be seen as far north as the Moray Firth and as far west as Argyll but the northern and western counties grow very small amounts. It is in the east, especially in the riverlands, where rainfall is light and sunshine great that wheat cultivation is at its fullest. The bulk of the crop comes from Fife, Perth, and Angus. For Scotland, as a whole, the yield per acre is often remarkably high and slightly higher than that for England and Wales. High yields may be accounted for by the urgent demand for home-grown foodstuffs and by the habit of farmers to allot their better land to this winter-sown crop. Only when Scottish wheat is mixed with Canadian types, however, can good bread flour be produced, but, by itself, it is suitable for the manufacture of a variety of biscuits which, in tins and packets, are distributed to a wide home and overseas market. Scotland produces about 50 per cent more wheat than in 1939.

Barley. Similar conditions of growth liken the distribution of barley to that of wheat except that there is an extension of this more robust grain northwards rather than westwards. It is in the eastern counties that barley is most successfully grown. Scottish farmers grow more barley than wheat. During the war and immediate post-war years there was a great extension of barley growing in all the eastern counties as far north as Ross-shire. This was the combined result of high prices, the introduction of more prolific varieties, the revival of liming (barley being particularly sensitive to soil acidity) and the suitability of this crop to combine harvesting. In yield per acre, the best returns are equal to those of East Anglia. Barley is spring sown and is in great use as a domestic foodstuff and as fodder. Most Scottish barley is unsuited for whisky making. Two thirds of the supplies come from East Anglia and there are imports from Australia and Canada. Scottish beer finds a ready sale at home and overseas while the United States of America is the great foreign purchaser of Scotch whisky.

Oats. This cereal, referred to as 'corn' in many parts of Scotland, is also spring sown and is the most popular grain crop. It does not appear to be so restricted by climate, altitude and other physical conditions. It is well grown in the colder north and in the wetter west and is particularly successful in the eastern and southern counties. Scotland's average yield per acre is slightly less than that of England and Wales. The main uses of oats are as a human food, e.g. in the form of porridge, and as fodder; there is a large despatch of oats to England and abroad in its processed form in packets and as loose oatmeal. A large quantity of oats is also sold to England in seed form. In some areas, e.g. in the north-east, the oat straw, strong as well as high in quality, is used for stock feeding and bedding.

ROOT CROPS

Of the common root crops grown in Scotland, the potato is easily the most suitable for its wide range of soil, altitude, and climate. It grows well in light and peaty soils but dislikes strong clays. Its greatest enemies are early autumn frosts and warm humid conditions which favour the spread of blight and certain pests. Scotland, as a whole, produces 1¼ million tons per year.

The coastal areas of Ayrshire, favoured with light soils and milder winters than other potato areas, produce most of Scotland's early potatoes, planted in February and coming on the market in June. The eastern arable counties, particularly Angus but also Perth and Fife, grow the main and late crops which go to the large cities and towns. Seed potato production is an important feature of Scottish farming. Scottish seed potatoes find a wide market all over England. In the early part of the year, coastal vessels carry seed potatoes from Angus to the counties around The Wash while considerable quantities from the west of Scotland are shipped to the Mediterranean countries, the Canary Isles and South Africa. The small potatoes or brock, as distinct from ware (i.e. domestic), are used locally to make up pig-feed.

The turnip is worthy of mention for the Scottish crop of 4½ million tons represents about 60 per cent of the total output of Great Britain. The growing of turnips, as distinct from mangolds which are far more popular south of the border, has always been important in Scottish agriculture for it is the regular winter feed of livestock, both indoors and out. Though the acreage in turnips is decreasing in Scotland, Aberdeen is still supreme in production. The other live-stock counties of Angus, Fife, Perth, Banff and Berwick also show large returns.

FRUIT AND VEGETABLES

The main fruit farms and horticultural stations are located in the Central Lowlands. Suitability of soil, freedom from damaging frosts, sheltered sites as well as proximity to populous areas are factors which determine their local position. Market gardening is an obvious activity near and on the outskirts of the four large cities but whereas Glasgow is forced to draw its supply from a radius beyond that of its own neighbourhood, Edinburgh manages to send produce grown in its vicinity to towns as far distant as Glasgow and Newcastle.

Mid-Clydesdale – the district around Lanark – not only eclipses all areas in glasshouse produce, especially tomatoes, but it is also a major fruit belt in which orchard and soft fruits are widely grown. Another zone, smaller in size but similar in type, exists in the neighbourhood of Ayr. Further north, in Strathmore and, less so, in the level Carse of Gowrie, entire fields are devoted to soft fruits such as raspberries. The ripening and picking of fruits are upwards of three weeks later than south of the border and, to a large extent, Scottish fruits do not encounter the full competition of consignments from England. Some of the crop is sold for domestic use but much fruit goes to Scottish jam factories.

Scottish farms, small in size as most of them are, make a substantial contribution to the production of food for the people of Great Britain. Although only a quarter of the total area may be deemed fertile, nevertheless the yields of Scotland's arable crops are among the highest in the world. Infertile though the mountain and hill lands are, they have been put to good use in rearing young animals either for fattening in the richer lowlands or for providing lowland farmers with suitable breeding animals. In this way, the more fertile land of the country can be more profitably utilised than if it were forced to rear all the young animals.

In part the success of farming in Scotland today may be attributed to the development of agricultural education and to the activities of the Scottish research stations, but there is no doubt that it is by dint of sheer application that Scottish farmers have been successful in the management of their land.

V · FISHING

SCOTLAND'S position on the north-west fringe of Europe has deprived her of many neighbours, but it has given her one resourceful and close friend: the North Sea. With a long coastline, and a high proportion of the population living near the sea, Scotland, like

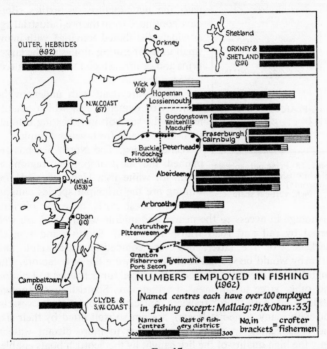

FIG. 17

Norway, gains some maritime compensations for the absence of those extensive lowlands and land contacts which occur further south in Europe. Fish have long been a major food resource where land is mountainous and the soil poor, and a major commodity of trade at home and abroad. Barrels of salted herrings and of salmon were among the most important of Scottish exports from very early times.

While fishing does not play such an important part in Scottish economy as it does in Norway's, it is relatively much more important than in England and Wales (three times as valuable per head of the population). In the long traditions of the Scottish fishing industry, both in supplementing agriculture and in developing trade, we may find comparisons with the manufacture of textiles. Both have continued from the pre-industrial age as widely distributed activities, with many small units operating alongside the larger firms and centres which modern resources have made possible.

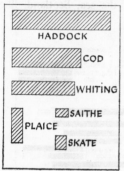

FIG. 18 Principal species of white fish landed: *weight*, horizontal scale; *price per cwt.*, vertical scale

Fisheries are dealt with under: white fishing (for demersal fish which usually feed on the sea bottom); herring fishing; shell-fishing; and fresh-water fishing.

White Fishing. The North Sea has remained the most important region of origin for white fish. Haddock, cod and whiting are the principal species caught. The east coast ports have an obvious advantage in access to the nearer and middle waters, and are well served by rail and road transport to both Scottish and English markets. For the latter, however, competition with Hull and Grimsby would be very difficult if these were the only factors. The English ports are more conveniently placed for deliveries to London and other large urban areas. Furthermore, Scottish fleets, though modernised (with motor trawlers replacing the older steam vessels, and with many seine-net boats), are not so well fitted by their size and organisation to make long voyages to more distant waters. Only the high quality of the fish caught by the Scottish boats enables them to find a ready market in England, and thus to maintain an industry which appears outmoded by its rivals. High costs of land transport and of new trawlers have caused anxiety for the future of the industry in north-east Scotland, but while the quality of the catch remains high so may the expectations of fishermen and merchants. The future of all British trawlers will be affected by the new

twelve-mile limits around Icelandic and Faroese coasts, and the
Scottish landings from these regions – already relatively small –
may decrease still further.

Two important aspects of the white fish industry are the use of
seine-net boats and the attraction of many of these boats to the
north and west of Scotland, where temperature changes have

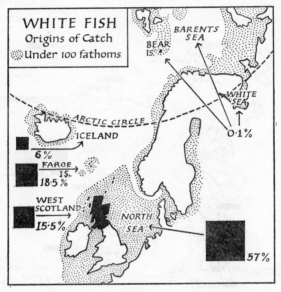

WHITE FISH
Origins of Catch
Under 100 fathoms.

BARENTS SEA
BEAR IS.
WHITE SEA
ARCTIC CIRCLE
ICELAND
0·1%
6%
FAROE IS.
18·5%
WEST SCOTLAND
15·5%
NORTH SEA
57%

FIG. 19

affected the distribution of fish. The small but modern seine-net
vessels suit the small ports of the north-east coast and the tradition
of individual ownership or co-partnership. They can be used for
either seine-netting or drift-net fishing for herring according to
choice. There has been a considerable increase in the number of
these fine vessels over the last twenty years or so, many having been
built with financial assistance from the Government since the end
of World War II. As a result boat builders in the smaller ports have
been kept employed.

From ports such as Buckie and Lossiemouth seine-net boats fish

overnight for a prime catch of white fish. The common practice is to
make landings at the home port and then forward the catch by road
to a larger centre – in particular Aberdeen – where wholesale
marketing is concentrated. (Some boats sailing from smaller ports
land directly at Aberdeen, however.)

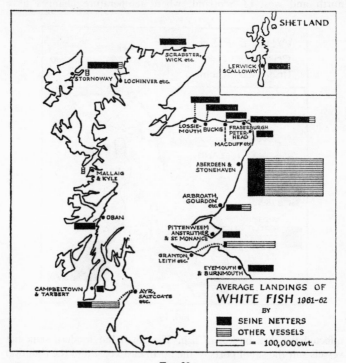

FIG. 20

Scotland's coasts and hinterlands provide a contrast between
east and west in fishing as in other human activities. The west coast
and islands share in the seine-net fishing for white fish, but only
account for about one-sixth of landings, and the greatest regional
concentration of the whole industry, both white fish and herring
fisheries, is in the north-east of Scotland, especially between Aberdeen and Lossiemouth.

Herring Fishing. The weight of herring landed in Scotland is greater than that of any other species of fish. (The next highest is haddock.) Diesel engined drifters have completely ousted the old steam drifters as herring fishing vessels. As distinct from the trawlers which generally use the same port the whole year round, herring drifters move from port to port according to the location of

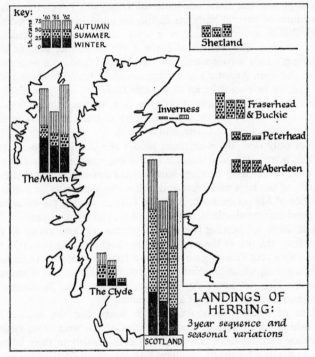

FIG. 21

the shoals, which visit different areas at different times. The avail- ability of packing and processing facilities also influences the choice of port. Centres which have quick-freezing plants, canning factories, large curing establishments, and factories for reducing herring to meal and oil, attract larger fleets than elsewhere. Such centres are to be found conveniently situated near each main fishing area.

On the west coast the rail-heads at Oban and at Mallaig, and the road to Ullapool, ensure a concentration of landings at these three ports. Stornoway is much less important than Ullapool for white fishing, but its herring catch is still considerable. (The total herring landings for the fishery district of Stornoway has been about a quarter that of Ullapool in recent years, while its white fish landings are less than one-tenth of Ullapool's.) Yet there is a multitude of natural harbours in the west and in such a region of agricultural poverty fishing is a vital activity for many coastal communities. The Minch and the Firth of Clyde, and smaller fishing grounds between, are protected by the islands and peninsulas from the open Atlantic and herring are to be found in these areas. Unlike the herring fisheries of the east there are heavy landings in winter as well as summer. Forty per cent. of the Scottish herring catch is landed in the three main fishery districts: Stornoway and Loch Broom, Firth of Clyde, and Mallaig.

Not only does the west coast favour the smaller seine-net and drifter boats, it is also distinct in the importance of the ring-net method of catching herring. Ring netters operate in the sheltered waters of the bays and inlets and follow the herring as far south as the Isle of Man. Greenock, Ayr, and Girvan, having the advantage of good communications, are the most frequently used ports in the Clyde area. All herring from the Clyde fishery, and about 50 per cent from the rest of the west coast are caught by ring nets. (On the east only a very little ring netting is now found in the Forth area, and it is trawling which supplements drifting for herring at Aberdeen. Scottish ring-net boats do, however, operate from Seahouses in Northumberland in August and September.)

Use of smaller harbours, smaller boats and the association of fishing with crofting, are all features of the west coast region. Although crofter-fishermen vary very considerably in their interest in the sea as a means of livelihood, they account for 10 per cent of those engaged full-time or part-time in the industry.

There has been a decline in the fishing industry of the Highlands and Islands. (Scotland's total herring catch was twice as big, pre-war, as in the years 1961-62, but Shetland's landings were then five times as large as in recent years.) Partly this is because there are not now so many boats fishing for herring, and partly because of poorer shoals in some areas. A decline in the number of crofter-fishermen has followed, and, with the continued loss of rural population from the crofting counties, it is not likely that the crofter-fisherman will ever again become as important in the economy of the western seaboard as he was in the past.

On the east coast the herring fleets fish in Shetland waters at the beginning of the summer and move south as the year progresses.

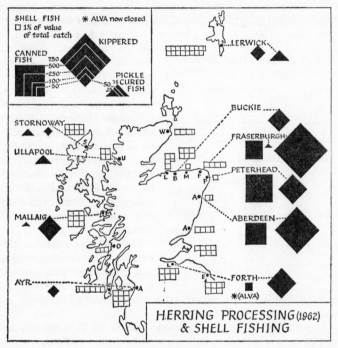

FIG. 22

The arrival and departure of the fleet in any area depends on the vagaries of the herring, but the seasons usually follow a rough timetable. Thus the Shetland fishing (Lerwick) lasts from May to July, and the north-east summer fishing (Fraserburgh, Peterhead, and Aberdeen) from June to August, the Yorkshire fishing lasts during August and September, and the East Anglian fishing (Great Yarmouth and Lowestoft) during October and November. It is quite common for two or three fishings to be proceeding simultaneously, as the season in one area overlaps that in another. Boats from the east generally join those of the west in the Minch for winter fishing (November to February).

The long term decline of herring fishing since the first world war has been accompanied by a decline in exports and a search for altern- ative home markets. Thus the supply of canned and frozen herring has developed (and this is true of the smaller export trade too), but even more striking are the amounts now going to pet-food and to the oil and meal reduction factories. These outlets for a catch which varies so much in size and quality, involve pro- cessing in fewer centres, with permanent factory establish- ments, whereas curing has been a dispersed and migratory activity of shore teams. Surplus supplies are usually absorbed in the oil and meal factories, though at a lower price than that paid for other means of disposal.

The map above indicates the location of processing works, and Fig. 23 shows the changes in marketing in recent years, but the fluctuations in supply make any one trend in disposal an unreliable guide for the future.

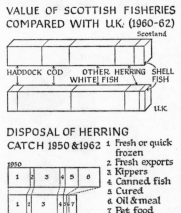

VALUE OF SCOTTISH FISHERIES COMPARED WITH U.K. (1960-62)

Scotland

HADDOCK COD   OTHER HERRING SHELL
              WHITE FISH   FISH

U.K.

DISPOSAL OF HERRING
CATCH 1950 &1962

1950

1. Fresh or quick frozen
2. Fresh exports
3. Kippers
4. Canned fish
5. Cured
6. Oil & meal
7. Pet food

1962

FIG. 23

Exports, including those packed fresh in ice (klondyked), are still of some importance, both those to European markets, and, on a smaller scale, to more distant lands (e.g. kippers to South Africa and canned herring to Australia).

Shell-Fishing. Though less than a tenth of the total value of all fish landed in Scotland, shell fish have increased more than twelve times in value in the last 25 years (while total value of all fish has only risen four times). They are of particular importance in the district of Lerwick (especially noted for lobsters), and in the Clyde and Minch. Recently the Norway lobster (known as prawns or scampi in the commercial world) has grown in importance, and it now rivals the familiar lobster for first place in value.

Fresh Water Fishing. The fame of Scotland for fishing does not rest entirely on herring and haddock, for in the rivers and firths there are renowned fresh-water fisheries. Salmon and sea-trout worth about £1 million are caught by rod and net every season. In addition to normal netting, fishing weirs are used in the southern river estuaries, and buoyed nets in some northern waters. The rod and line catch represents more than the fish, for it is part of the wider tourist industry, too.

VI · FORESTRY

ONE-THIRD of the woodlands of Great Britain is located in Scotland. Such a portion, large though it may appear, is meagre in comparison with the great forests that used to cover the face of Scotland in primeval days. In fact, the woodland area of Scotland represents only 6·6 per cent of the total area of the country and falls very far short of 20 per cent, the accepted optimum for the economy of a country. Not many European countries have such a small proportion of woodland.

During the first half of this century, the deliberate felling of great areas of woodland helped to meet the increasing demands for timber, rendered urgent on the occasion of the two wars. Most of this timber was obtained from the forests of private owners who now own most of the woodlands of Scotland. The remainder is controlled by the Forestry Commission in whom has been vested official forest authority since 1919. In their post-war plan (1946) of tree planting, Scotland is responsible for developing not less than half of the 5 million acres of productive woodland of Great Britain. This project, apportioned to private owners as well as to the Commission, is to extend over the next 50 years.

The counties with the largest percentage of land area devoted to woodland are Moray (21·6 per cent), and Nairn (19·1 per cent) but five other counties in the north and east have a percentage of 10-15 per cent. In some western and northern districts, high altitude and infertile soils restrict growth and the amount of woodland is therefore low. In Caithness it is only 0·4 per cent and in the Orkney and Shetland Isles there is hardly any woodland at all. On the poorer land and on land wholly unfit for any other activity, state forests are being established. One large forest is in the Loch Ard district of the Trossachs. In the Loch Awe area, 5,000 acres of forest are being developed. On the Culbin sands of the Moray coast, a remarkable undertaking has been accomplished. A mattress of branches was laid down to restrict the movement of sand dunes and what was formerly a useless waste has now been converted into several thousands of acres of pine trees.

Of the two tree types, broad-leaved (hardwood) and conifers

(softwood), the latter is more common in Scottish woodlands. The coniferous forests of Scotland cover more than four times as much territory as the broad-leaved. The new state forests are particularly devoted to the development of conifers. The Scots pine (sometimes called the Scots fir) covers the greatest area in Scotland. This is the only conifer that is indigenous to Scotland. It can grow in most soils other than peat and can endure rough winter conditions. On suitable soils its growth is fairly rapid and it can grow to about 100 feet. The pine is just as common in private as in state forests.

Yet the spruce ranks first in order of planting in Scotland today. It is clearly the favourite in the younger state forests. There are two types – the Sitka spruce, an exotic tree, originating in the Pacific coastal area of North America and more numerous than the Norway spruce which is of European origin. The spruce, which is the festive Christmas tree, thrives in peaty soils and is suited to the heavy rainfall of the west of Scotland. It is a fast grower, pointed in shape at its top and retains its needles

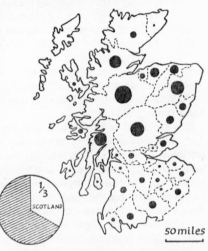

FIG. 24 (*Left*) Woodlands of Great Britain. (*Right*) Total woodland area of Scotland to total land area. ● Woodland plotted to scale of map

for several years. The other important softwood is the larch, both European and Japanese types, whose seed may be obtained at home, from Europe and from Japan. The larch, also rapid in growth, is not evergreen; its leaves appear in spring. It is common throughout Scotland. The Corsican pine and the Douglas fir, the latter originally from the Pacific coast of North America, are also grown in lesser quantities.

Almost all the future trees of Scotland start off as transplants grown from seed, collected or imported, in the Forestry Commission's nurseries at Newton near Elgin, Kirroughtree near Newton

Stewart, Ledmore near Perth or at Tulliallan near Alloa. The seed has to be procured and sown one or two or even four years in advance of the plants being required for forest use. The young plants may be transplanted more than once in the nursery before being finally transferred, at the end of two or more years, to the selected plantation. Planting is a winter task and goes on from November to March, during which time the tree is in its winter rest period. Every year a noticeable increase in planting new forests can be recorded. This progress is in part due to the use of the tractor with extra-wide fitting tracks, which, by means of a strong and deep blade, turns the turf over and trees are planted on the upturned turf, thereby gaining the advantage of the humus derived from the decaying surface vegetation. It is not before 12-20 years have elapsed that the first thinnings are taken from a forest, i.e. the young trees are removed to allow the others to attain fuller stature. The final and most productive yield from a coniferous forest does not come for 70-80 years and hardwoods do not provide a full harvest until they are a century old.

It is from the private forests and the thinnings of state forests that the home supplies of timber are now derived. Home-grown softwood, pine, and spruce, is chiefly used for making packing cases, telegraph poles, posts, stakes, and fencing, but the better quality is suitable for structural purposes in houses and other buildings. Its most important use, however, is in the form of pit-props of various sizes. Almost half of the pit-props used in Scottish mines are home supplied and some North of England mines also receive part of their supplies from Scotland.

The extraction of thinnings and the construction of roads to the new forests are but two of the great demands on manpower in forestry activities. There is a real labour problem in the industry, for it has to compete with agricultural and fishing pursuits as well as the new hydro-electric projects, all in areas with a scanty population. One of the ways by which it is hoped to attract workers to forestry is the provision of houses erected at selected points in remote areas. Well known is the village of Ae in Dumfriesshire. It is a forest settlement, complete with 100 houses, school, church, shops, etc. Similar villages exist in other parts of Scotland. By the creation of such communities, people may be drawn to the rural and remote parts of the country.

The tree planting programme, now in progress, creates conflicting claims on the use of land for trees and for sheep. Much success has attended sheep farming in some highland and upland areas and the output, in terms of food production, is high. Yet the great demands for timber and the acute shortage of home-grown supplies render it imperative that blocks or acreages of new trees should be planted in what has been regarded as sheep-grazing territory. The existence of forests provides valuable shelter to stock and crop land. The humus content of the soil is maintained and the risk of soil erosion reduced. Moreover, forestry operations encourage a higher rate of settled population than does sheep farming. Before large areas are assigned to the production of timber in such a way to ensure the minimum reduction in sheep population, careful planning is essential and co-operation between farmer and forester very desirable.

At Annat Point, Corpach on Loch Eil near Fort William, a new pulp and paper mill is nearing completion. This is the biggest industrial project started in the Highlands since the war. The mill, using 5,000 tons of Scottish softwood every week, will provide work for over 2,000 men and women. The mill is well located. It is within reasonable distance of many softwood forests. There is an abundance of water for processing. The tidal waters of Loch Eil and Loch Linnhe will sweep away the mill's effluent. A main road runs past the mill and the West Highland railway is available on a long term basis. The mill is engaged in pulp making as well as in the manufacture of paper. Its raw material is softwood timber, its finished product is in the form of huge paper rolls. The existence of such a mill is most significant. It provides a useful product and gives a fresh stimulus to forestry. Employment is available in a new type of work and this helps to stem the drift of people from the Highlands. The new mill is an indication of the integration of forestry and industry, a unity that is surely beneficial to the economy of Scotland.

VII · COAL MINING

Production and distribution. Practically all the coal resources are located in one region of the country, the Central Lowlands. Fortunate as such a concentration has been to Scotland, over the last two centuries, a more general distribution of coal would also have brought economic advantages to the other two regions of the country. The proved and workable seams exist at present in an area that stretches, south-west to north-east, from the Ayrshire coast to South and East Fife. They can be grouped into four main coal mining areas:

Coal Mining Area	Output in million tons	
	1950	1963
1. Fife and Clackmannan	7·3	6·4
2. Lothians	3·8	3·2
3. Central Coalfield (extending over Lanarkshire, Stirlingshire, West Lothian, and Dunbartonshire)	7·8	3·2
4. Ayrshire (including North Dumfriesshire)	4·4	3·7
	23·3	16·5

A small coalfield is worked at Machrihanish in southern Kintyre and a little coal is found and worked in the Brora district of the Moray Firth.

The present output in Scotland is around 16½ million tons. This tonnage which is a considerable reduction compared to the early part of the century (e.g. in 1913, 42 million tons), represents over 8 per cent of the total output of Great Britain. There are now 56,000 miners in Scotland (just over 10 per cent of the total number in Great Britain).

For the last two centuries, coal has been indispensable to the growing economy of Scotland. A plentiful supply, well placed in regard to the Clyde and Forth outlets of trade and close to or combined with quantities of iron ore, was especially favourable to the industries that made the industrial revolution in Scotland. Coal was synonymous with power, steam power, the essential source of industrial energy. The Central coalfield was a most productive area; year in, year out, from the collieries of Lanarkshire there came an assured supply of coals.

Now the coal mining industry of Scotland is passing through a phase of reconstruction and redevelopment. Many pits in the Central, Fife and Ayrshire areas have closed or are about to cease mining operations. Some pits are undergoing reconstruction, e.g. at Newtongrange in the Lothians. Where reserves are particularly rich and durable, there are new sinkings as at Killoch (Ayrshire)

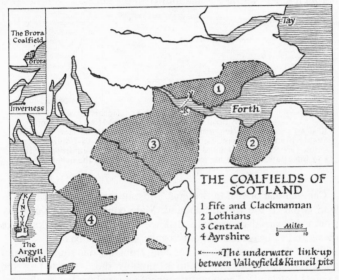

FIG. 25 (*Crown copyright reserved*)

Bilston Glen (Lothians) and Seafield near Kirkcaldy. An important advance, of recent date, has been the completion of a tunnel under the river Forth linking the Kinneil pit at Bo'ness with Valleyfield pit in south Fife. By this convenient under-river link-up, Valleyfield coal may be brought more quickly to the surface at Bo'ness, south of the river.

The most productive coal seams exist generally at great depths from 2-3000 feet below the surface. The only effective way of extracting coals at such levels is by the construction of very large mining units (4-5000 tons output per day) and by the application of horizon mining methods as, for example, in the Monktonhall colliery in the

Lothians. By this method, the coal is cut mechanically and power loading machinery moves the coal to the vertical shaft where it is brought to the surface by powerful electric winders, capable of raising coal to the surface from the depth of 2000 feet in less than a minute. Such modern methods of mining as mechanical coal cutters, power loading machines and electric winding gear result in speedy output and less wastage of manpower in the mines.

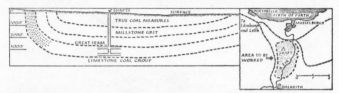

Fig. 26 Planned horizon mining in Midlothian. The advantages of this site are: (i) Shafts centrally positioned in coal basin. (ii) High production from 12 deep seams. (iii) Rich seams between 2,700 and 3,600 feet. (iv) Good quality domestic and industrial coal. (v) Convenient to Edinburgh and Leith. (vi) Railways at hand for easy disposal. (vii) Fair freedom from housing estates and subsidence problems. (viii) near to the new Cockenzie power station.

Consumption of coal in Scotland. Most of the coal mined in Scotland is put to use within Scotland. Main consumers are electricity works, industrial concerns and domestic users. Gas works, coke ovens and railways also require regular supplies of coal.

By far the greatest demand for coal, from any one source, is from the electricity producing stations, notably those situated in the Central Lowlands. The quantity of coal required for the production of electricity in Scotland has risen substantially over the last few years. The coal-fired stations of the South of Scotland Electricity Board consume almost 5 million tons of coal annually. The demand for coal will be even greater, possibly doubled, in the near future when the new steam fired electricity plants are in full production at Cockenzie, Longannet and Methil.

Domestic consumers continue to make great demands on coal supplies but their requirements have decreased in recent years. This is mainly because of the great increase in the use of electric fires and of the various forms of central heating. In large cities such as Glasgow, where smokeless zones have been created, many householders have adopted electric or gas means of heating their homes.

At one time industry was the greatest consumer of coal but now there are greater demands on electricity. Since electricity and industry are so closely related, the role of the new electricity producing stations in increasing and sustaining the power potential for industry is abundantly clear.

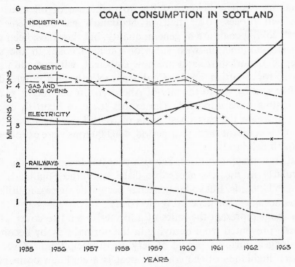

With acknowledgment to the South of Scotland Electricity Board

FIG. 27

The withdrawal of steam driven locomotives and their replacement by diesel and electric trains has been most significant in the realm of rail transport in Scotland. In consequence, the amount of coal, required for locomotive traction, has suffered a steady decrease within recent years. Railways are the least important of the main consumers of coal.

Gas works rely on a steady supply of coal. In addition to numerous local gas works, Scotland now possesses the first Lurgi gas-making plant in use in Great Britain. It is in operation at Westfield, near Loch Leven. Its supply of low quality coal is derived from an opencast mine on the spot. (At an opencast mine, seams outcrop near the surface and mining is rather like quarrying.) The gas made at Westfield is passed into the general gas grid of Central Scotland by long distance pipelines which distribute gas to Dundee by a pipe across the Tay railway bridge and to the Glasgow and Kilmarnock areas by a river-bed pipe under the Forth near Kincardine. (Note, also, that at Provan, Glasgow, at Kilmarnock and Granton, modern gas-making plant is being installed to make use of oil feedstock which will process over half of Scotland's gas requirements). Scottish coking coals are of general quality, but they have been very useful (in conjunction with superior Durham coke) in the steel centres of Lanarkshire, and are now sufficient, without additional imports, for Scottish needs. Coal from North East England is regularly sent by sea to the city of Aberdeen. In one recent year, $\frac{1}{4}$ million tons were imported. The export trade in Scottish coal is mainly through the east coast ports of Methil, Grangemouth and Leith. Over a recent three year period, 440,000 tons were exported to the North Sea lands.

Peat. For many centuries, Scottish peat has been a familiar fuel, particularly in the less accessible districts of the Highlands and Southern Uplands. But so far there has been little success in utilising peat as an agent for generating electricity.

Peat bogs represent the relics of a former vegetative cover which has been prevented from decaying in the normal way by becoming water-logged during a period of very great precipitation. Over the northern highlands of the country, peat is a common occurrence, with an average depth of 8 feet, but in Perthshire, Stirlingshire, Ayrshire, and the Solway counties, there are also peat bogs, large in area and with an average depth of 14 feet.

The Geological Survey estimates that there are about $1\frac{1}{2}$ million acres of peat at an average of 8 feet in depth. About 600 million tons of peat, dry weight, are believed to exist in mosses with a depth and accessibility to permit of exploitation. This tonnage is equivalent to 500 million tons of coal or, at present annual production, thirty years' output.

It is the crofter who normally depends on peat mosses for much of his domestic fuel. The peat, black or brown in appearance, is hand-cut during the drier spell of spring and summer. The peat blocks, like bricks in size, are then set up to dry by the action of the wind and the sun before being carried or carted to the crofters' cottages, there to be stored in the open under cover, in an outshed or stacked against a warm gable wall.

Peat cutting, a seasonal occupation, is and has always been a slow, wet and laborious task. Peat drying depends on the state of the weather. In the future utilisation of peat on a large scale, and as an all-the-year-round pursuit, two problems are manifest. A method has still to be devised whereby peat can be obtained mechanically at minimum cost. Furthermore, because the moisture content of peat is as high as 90 per cent, the greater problem, yet to be solved, is to discover an efficient artificial means of driving off the water.

The conversion of peat-covered land to useful agricultural purposes is one immediate result derived from lifting an overlay of peat, but it is also possible, as in some European lands, to make use of peat fibre as stable litter and as a soil conditioner in horticulture, e.g. in the propagation of bulbs in glasshouses. This is already being done in Scotland. The major value of peat is in the distilling of whisky. After its first soaking in water and heating, malting barley – the raw material of the distiller – is dried in a kiln, easily recognised in a distillery by its pinnacle shaped tower. There, with peat reek rising through a perforated floor from the peat fire below, the barley is dried. It is this drying of the malting barley by means of a peat fire which helps to give the whisky its distinctive flavour and character.

VIII · ELECTRICITY

In every human activity in Scotland, as elsewhere, there is a constant demand for more energy to replace or supplement human efforts. Great as it is and has been, steam power must, perforce, accept electricity as a partner, if not indeed, as a rival form of energy. By electric lines and cables, electricity may be transmitted long distances conveniently and speedily. Electricity, also, provides a formidable trio in the modern world – light, heat and power.

In Scotland, today, water, coal, oil and, recently, atomic power are all agents used in the production of electricity. The development of hydro-electric schemes in Scotland was slow and only a few were established before the late 1940s. The earliest Scottish hydro-electric power schemes at Falls of Foyers (1895), the first big hydro station in Great Britain, and at Kinlochleven (1905) were private arrangements between the landowners and the British Aluminium Co. for the use of local water. Twenty years later, despite opposition, larger schemes were completed in Lochaber, in the Grampians and in Galloway.

The steam or coal fired stations that produce electricity are located mostly in the central part of Scotland where coal measures are exploited. Scottish diesel stations are small generating units. They are widely distributed over the northern part of the country. The nuclear plant of the Atomic Energy Authority at Chapelcross, Annan, passes some electricity into the national grid. Now, from the new Hunterston Nuclear Generating station, electricity is starting to flow and, when in full operation, its output is expected to provide about a quarter of the electricity required in the south of Scotland. It is an ultra-modern plant, the first of its kind, with no cooling towers or coal stocks and using huge quantities of nearby sea water for cooling purposes.

In 1947, the electricity supply industry was nationalised under the name of the British Electricity Authority with area boards. The North of Scotland Hydro-electric Board, established to develop Highland water, is independent because of the special problems of its area. It controls that part of Scotland which lies north of a Clyde-Tay boundary. The South of Scotland Electricity Board is responsible

54

for the rest of Scotland. Both boards generate, transmit and supply electricity to consumers in their own area and, when necessary, to each other and to zones outside Scotland.

THE NORTH OF SCOTLAND

Two major stations, at Aberdeen and Dundee, use steam plant. A number of diesel oil stations exist on the islands or at less accessible points on the mainland. The Highland hydro-electric stations are of the greatest importance. The Highlands possess the physical advantages of altitude and abundance of lochs. They experience greater precipitation than their counterparts elsewhere in Great Britain. The counties of Inverness, Ross and Cromarty, Perth, Argyll, and Sutherland each receive a very high amount of rainfall and snow. They thus contain the best catchment or receiving areas for the collection of water for electricity requirements. About 50 per cent. of the run-off flows down the rivers in October, November, December, and January, the time of the year when maximum demands are made on electricity. But, unlike the rivers of Switzerland or Norway, which receive copious supplies of melting snow and ice every year, those of Scotland may yield a precariously small amount of water in April, May and June when there is low rainfall along with much evaporation. Hydro-electric schemes in the Highlands overcome such a threat of water shortage by trapping water from one watershed and transferring it by tunnels or aqueducts to a parent reservoir.

The map on page 56 shows the location of the hydro-generating stations of Scotland now in operation. Four points are noteworthy about electricity production in the north of Scotland:

1. There is a great concentration of hydro-stations in the Highlands.
2. The output has risen very rapidly over a very short and recent period. (See table overleaf.)
3. Production by water power has more than doubled during ten years and far exceeds both steam and diesel generation.
4. Total production in the North of Scotland, by water, steam and diesel means, now represents over a quarter of the total output of electricity in Scotland.

North of Scotland						Millions of units generated	
						1953	1963
Water power	.	.	.	.	.	944	2210
Steam	.	.	.	.	.	364	318
Diesel	.	.	.	.	.	55	84
						1363	2612
Scotland (whole)		.	.	.	.	5696	11854

THE HYDRO-ELECTRIC STATIONS OF SCOTLAND

FIG. 28

New power stations, with transmission and distribution facilities, are still being planned and built to meet an increasing demand for electricity. The pumped storage scheme at Cruachan, Loch Awe,

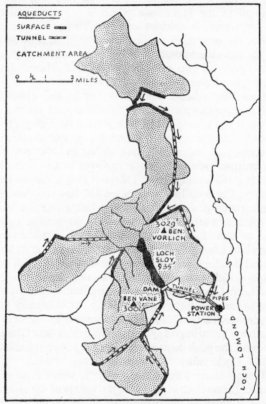

FIG. 29 The Loch Sloy hydro-electric scheme

with its underground power station and the steam power station at the east end of Dundee are two projects likely to provide a substantial increase in electricity in the North of Scotland.

The Central Lowlands of Scotland cannot therefore be regarded as having the monopoly of the natural power resources of the

5

country. In the economy of Scotland, it is as important to recognise the value of the water resources of the Highlands as it is to emphasise the coal reserves of the Lowlands. Moreover, extraction of coal hastens, inevitably, the exhaustion of local measures whereas the high rainfall of the Highlands, which is a more permanent or natural occurrence, is renewed annually. There is no more fitting example of the subjection of the natural conditions of an area to human use than the utilisation of the waters of the Highlands. A brief description of two of the hydro-electric schemes illustrates this geographical point.

The Loch Sloy scheme. Loch Sloy lies to the west of Loch Lomond in mountainous country with an annual rainfall of over 100 inches. It is a typical glacial loch set in a deep gorge. Its catchment area has been extended by trapping a number of other streams and diverting their waters into the loch. At its lower end, a dam – the first buttress type to be made in Great Britain – was built of concrete. It is 160 feet high, over 1,000 feet long and is the biggest in the country. The loch has been raised 150 feet and thus enlarged into a great storage reservoir over 700 feet above sea level. The natural catchment area of the loch was 6½ square miles. Today, rain falling in an area of 32 square miles is diverted by tunnels and open aqueducts into Loch Sloy. The water leaves the loch at its lower end by a tunnel 2 miles long and passes through Ben Vorlich into four huge pipes which descend to the generating station on the west shore of Loch Lomond. The force of the water, in its descent, is sufficient to turn the turbines which drive the machinery that produces hydro-electricity. This power, transmitted by overhead cables, passes into the Scottish grid system at Windyhills near Glasgow and helps to meet the peak demands for electric power in the industrial area of the Clyde valley.

The Tummel-Garry scheme. This scheme, which is an extension of an earlier hydro-electric project in the valleys of the rivers Garry and Tummel, involves much diversion of water and construction of many miles of tunnels. Water is collected from a huge catchment area of the Highlands in central Perthshire with an average annual rainfall of over 50 inches. A tunnel, 12 miles long, conducts water from many streams to a new reservoir constructed in the upper part of Glen Errochty. Another tunnel, 6 miles long, transfers the water to the Errochty power station at the western end of Loch Tummel.

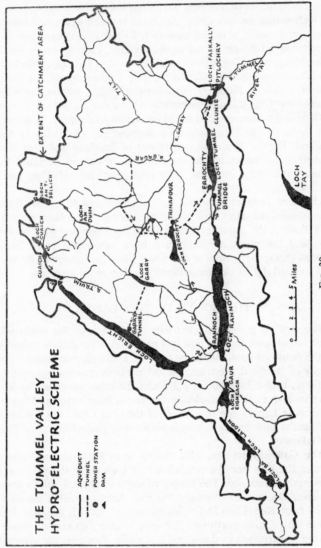

THE TUMMEL VALLEY
HYDRO-ELECTRIC SCHEME

AQUEDUCT
TUNNEL
POWER STATION
DAM

0 1 2 3 4 5 Miles

FIG. 30

At the eastern end of this loch, a dam has been made which enlarges the loch and raises its surface level by 15 feet and converts it into a reservoir. From it, a tunnel aqueduct, 23 feet in diameter and the largest water bearing tunnel in the country, conveys water for 2 miles down to the Clunie power station on Loch Faskally. This loch has been created in the valley of the river Tummel by the construction of a dam at Pitlochry. Here another power station has been established. Thus this scheme embraces three dams and three power stations and makes repeated use of the same water supply. Together, they help to meet the increasing demand for electricity in the southern Highlands and the north-east of Scotland and they also contribute to the industrial requirements of central Scotland by passing electricity into the grid system at Bonnybridge, near Falkirk.

The river Tummel is famous for its salmon and to enable them to surmount the dams, fish passes or stairways have been erected. At Pitlochry, the water level rises 18 inches from one pool to the next and the pools are connected by a submerged pipe. Glass windows set into the sides of two pools allow the salmon to be seen and counted, by an electronic device, as they move upstream.

THE SOUTH OF SCOTLAND

The striking growth of electricity production in the Highlands must not obscure the fact that it is produced in far greater quantity in the South of Scotland, some of it by hydro-electric means. The South of Scotland Electricity Board controls nineteen generating stations; twelve have steam plant and the other seven are hydro-electric. Two small hydro-electric stations at Bonnington and Stonebyres near Lanark use the waters of the river Clyde but the most spectacular and productive hydro-scheme is that of the river Dee in Galloway.

The Galloway scheme. This project is in Kirkcudbright where neither the hills nor the rainfall are as high as in the two areas previously mentioned. The supply of water is derived chiefly from the river Dee and its tributary, the river Ken containing the elongated Loch Ken. Loch Doon, whose normal outlet is into the river Doon which flows north into Ayrshire, is also part of the scheme. By the construction of dams and a pipeline, its waters are diverted

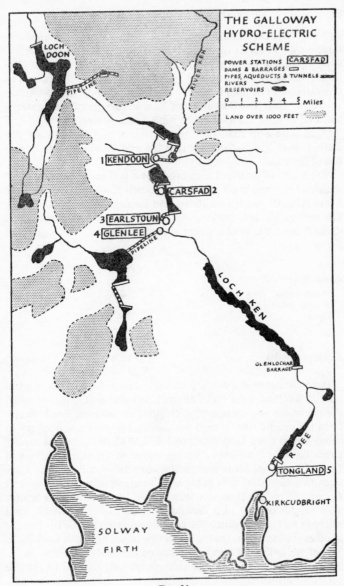

THE GALLOWAY
HYDRO-ELECTRIC
SCHEME

POWER STATIONS CARSFAD
DAMS & BARRAGES
PIPES, AQUEDUCTS & TUNNELS
RIVERS
RESERVOIRS

0 1 2 3 4 5 Miles

LAND OVER 1000 FEET

LOCH
DOON

PIPELINE

RIVER KEN

1 KENDOON

CARSFAD 2

3 EARLSTOUN
4 GLENLEE

PIPELINE

LOCH KEN

GLENLOCHAR
BARRAGE

R DEE

TONGLAND 5

KIRKCUDBRIGHT

SOLWAY

FIRTH

Fig. 31

into the Ken-Dee valley to augment the flow of water draining southwards. A series of dams, built at intervals along this valley, store up water to supply no less than five power stations. The water, discharged from the highest station at Kendoon, passes downstream to be used in turn by the other stations. At Glenlochar where the river Dee leaves Loch Ken, a barrage of steel gates is required to raise the level of the water of Loch Ken and to control its final release to the lowest power station at Tongland. All five stations pass hydro-electricity into the grid system for use in and out of Scotland.

The South of Scotland area produces about three quarters of all the electricity produced in Scotland. Apart from the output of the hydro-schemes mentioned above, and the supply now coming from Hunterston Nuclear station, the great proportion of electricity is derived from the twelve steam stations located in the Clyde and Forth areas.

		Millions of units generated	
South of Scotland		1953	1963
Water power		278	308
Steam		4085	8934
Diesel		—	—
		4363	9242
Scotland (whole)		5696	11854

But new steam stations are already taking shape in the central part of Scotland. Like sticks of chalk, two 400 foot chimneys mark the site of the new station at Kincardine on the river Forth. Water from the nearby river is used for cooling purposes and a supply of suitable coal from local mines in Fife and Clackmannan is readily available. This is an important newcomer to the steam stations of Central Scotland. More and similar ones are to follow. Ash waste from this very station is being used to create a reclaimed area at Longannet on the foreshore east of the Kincardine road bridge. This neighbour will also depend on local coal. At Methil, coal slurry (a sort of wet, putty-like coal preparation) will be the fuel for another station-to-be. On the south side of the Forth, at Cockenzie, east of Musselburgh, another reclaimed area is being prepared for a further steam station. These stations are well situated to provide a source of power to an area of developing industrial growth. When all such stations are in full production, the supply of electricity in Scotland, from steam units, will be substantially increased.

The uses of electricity. The uses to which electricity can be put are far too numerous and well known to be enumerated at length. In the large cities and urban districts, the consumers are of many types, but especially heavy are the requirements of industrial units, e.g. iron and steel works, jute mills, aluminium works, paper mills, ice works, textile factories, bakeries, and canneries. The number of domestic appliances that are available is an index of the usefulness and popularity of electricity in the home. But for electricity, the municipal and wider means of communication like trains, trolley buses, underground, radio, television, and telephone services would not function. A supply of power that is easily transmitted by cable is a prerequisite of the modern equipment used in Scottish coal mines. Electric lifting gear is regularly used in loading and discharging cargoes at Scottish ports.

Highland hydro-electricity, transported over miles of overhead cables, is of great use in urban centres. In the rural districts and more remote parts of the country, the value of an electrical supply has been and still is significant, if less noticeable. Power from the early Highland schemes governed the location of the aluminium works at Lochaber, Kinlochleven, and Foyers. In the modern method of obtaining aluminium ingots from raw alumina, an enormous and assured inexpensive local supply of electrical power is essential.

Within the last few years, a supply of electricity has been brought to farms, to crofts and to cottages of farm and forestry workers. Many are the crofts in the north of Scotland that are connected to an electrical supply. By submarine cables, which now carry electricity six miles to the island of Jura, it is intended to provide the islanders of Barra, North Uist and others in the Shetland and Orkney groups with a supply of electricity. In South West Scotland, most dairy farmers have electrical appliances in their farmsteads. In a number of northern farms, successful experiments in drying grass and hay by electrical power have been carried out. Rural industries are using electrical means, e.g. a dehydrated vegetable plant at Errol, a pottery at Strachur (Argyll), a refrigeration plant of an Argyllshire farm growing white heather. In one way or another, through the development of hydro-electric schemes, most people in the Highlands and Southern Uplands are becoming more familiar with and are readily acknowledging the benefits of a supply of electricity.

Moreover, the development of such schemes has created a demand for the special equipment used in the installation and maintenance of dams and power stations. Local quarried stone has been used in several places for the erection of dams and power houses while in Glasgow, Edinburgh, Clydebank, and Dundee, there are now factories engaged in the production of turbines and other technical plant not only for the Scottish schemes but for similar ones in the Commonwealth and elsewhere abroad.

IX · MANUFACTURING

IT has already been noted how important manufacturing is among Scottish industries, and the account of coal mining goes far in explaining why this should be so. Resources of power would have ensured the development of manufacturing industries had no other factors operated. But the presence of deep waterways in central Scotland, while allowing easier export of coal, allows too for the import of raw materials and the export of manufactured goods.

The location of coalfields and estuaries close together make power and trade available to the whole region, and one might expect almost any industry to flourish there. In fact there is a wide range of manufacturing in central Scotland, and in many ways this shows a trend which is true for the country as a whole, giving it a national status industrially, rather than the status of a mere province or region of Great Britain. This diversity in manufacturing, already noted in its broad regional variations (*Manpower:* pp 20-21) calls for more careful study in terms of both distribution and development.

The different parts of Scotland show considerable specialisation in fact, particularly outwith the west Central Lowlands, and great emphasis must be placed on a few major industries and on a few important centres of manufacture. The reasons for the diversity of products must be sought in both economic and political history, and in the geographical background which includes strong features of isolation and variety of resources. Similarly the reasons for both specialisation in type of manufacture and localisation in distribution of industry are those of historical-geography. Sites for factories which are nearest coal and navigable water have an overall advantage. Towns which developed local industries before the industrial revolution have traditions of skill linking the past and present. The location of the settlements at bridges, defensive sites, etc., underlies the distribution of industry today, for there can be few factories which have grown up in isolation from all previous settlements.

The making of iron and steel, and shipbuilding, bring out very strongly the factors of coalfields and estuaries, and the characteristics of heavy industry in general which dominates the Central Lowlands. Textiles are the most striking link between past and present, the older use of native resources underlying the industry throughout all regions. These industries are described in more detail therefore, but it must be remembered that they account for less than a third of all workers employed in manufacturing. Engineering industries other than shipbuilding are not summarised here, although they are particularly important in Scotland: the range of products and variety of factors lead more naturally to treatment in the regional geography of Scotland. While some specialisations – such as boiler-making – remain important, others have declined (e.g. locomotive-building), and newer ones have arisen (e.g. earth-moving equipment). Otherwise it is sufficient to point out that in many towns engineering is a secondary industry, or arose as such, meeting the demands of other local industries. The manufacture of textile machinery and paper-making machinery are two examples of this.

One other generalisation can be made here, since it applies to a wide range of industries and centres: viz. the importance of water supplies, both in quantity and quality. We are accustomed to think of the pre-industrial water-power of many rivers and burns, replaced today by coal in the Lowlands and transformed into electricity in the Highlands. But while it is true that little direct use of water for power continues in modern factories, the quality of water available for many processes, e.g. in brewing, distilling, paper-making, and a wide range of textile and chemical operations, and the quantity of water for other industrial purposes (e.g. steam power, cooling and washing operations), both remain very important. The disposal of industrial waste-products also means that river-side locations are preferred. When we link these needs to those which have historically affected the growth of settlements, we find a persistent pattern in the location of industry in which one element of the physical environment – the river – is dominant.

Decay and New Growth. The well established industrial estates, e.g. Hillington, near Glasgow, and Sighthill, Edinburgh, which have widened the range of Scotland's manufactures, are being supplemented by new ones, e.g. Polmadie, Glasgow, and Bellshill, Lanarkshire. But the problem of congestion in the older urban areas calls for more complete replanning, and new towns have been developed therefore, at East Kilbride, Glenrothes and Cumbernauld. (A fourth at Livingston is in the early stages of construction.) Together with the 'overspill' population from Glasgow, being settled in smaller towns, such as Haddington, these new centres of growing population widen the distribution of new industrial enterprise.

But, even so, the 'second industrial revolution', which is required to remedy the imbalance of the first, is seen to be too piecemeal and incomplete. Only in a few centres – the most notable being Grangemouth – has there been a steady growth of modern industry with a cluster of new subsidiary manufactures. Modern planning aims to hinge Scotland's industrial future to the areas of new growth, with better support in communications, water-supplies and power supplies. More detail of these developments will be considered later, but it is to be noted immediately in thinking of Scotland's manufactures: the old and the new are stages in an incomplete evolution.

THE IRON AND STEEL INDUSTRY

The iron and steel industry is given first place in this review of Scottish manufacturing not only because of its intrinsic importance but also because it supports so many other industries. In particular it supplies the most vital materials to the shipbuilding and other engineering industries for which the country is famous, and which have made Scotland a land of heavy industry.

The manufacture of iron and steel requires the assembly of large quantities of fuel and raw material, the latter including iron ore and limestone for blast-furnaces, and pig iron and scrap metal (iron and steel) for steel furnaces. An ideal site for the industry would have ready access to these materials (and to a good water supply), and it would also have three human assets: skilled labour, capital for investment, and nearby markets for its products.

In Britain as a whole, the industry has sought sites where fuel and ore have been available, the human assets have then developed and given more permanence to these locations – industrial inertia. Before the Industrial Revolution the forests which provided timber for charcoal were the main attraction to iron smelters. During the Industrial Revolution coalfields formed the new bases of rapidly expanding iron production, wherever coal was suitable for smelting, and often iron ore was found in the same areas. Scotland found these raw materials in the 'splint' coal and 'blackband' ores. (Splint coal did not break up during smelting, and the blackband ores had the advantage of being found in close association with coal and lime-stone).

Iron. First Falkirk and then the middle Clyde valley developed large iron works in the late eighteenth and nineteenth centuries. The researches of Neilson in 1828 resulted in the efficient use of these local ores by means of a hot blast. In the mid-nineteenth century Scotland was producing about a quarter of Britain's iron, with works at Carron, near Falkirk, in the east; at Coatbridge, Airdrie, Motherwell, Wishaw, and Glasgow – the main central group; and at Irvine, Kilbirnie, Lugar, and Muirkirk in north Ayrshire.

While the twentieth century has seen the exhaustion of worth-while ores in all the coalfields of Britain, in Scotland both iron ore and the special splint coal have been used up (in any case the latter is unsuited for use in modern furnaces). Thus the manufacture of iron suffered a severe set-back. Production fell from more than one and one-third million tons in 1913 to half a million tons between 1920 and 1930. Research then made possible the production of a suitable coke from Scottish coal with a small addition of Durham coal, and ore was imported via the Clyde and Forth. But iron manu-facture has not flourished in Scotland in this century in proportion to the thriving steel industry which grew up beside it. For the steel industry there is the stimulus of the demand from shipbuilders and other manufacturers, and the large deficit in pig iron supplies for steel making has been balanced by imported and local scrap metal supplies. One important source of scrap metal is the shipbreaking industry, and the shipbreakers' yards along the Gare Loch play a major part in maintaining a good supply of this vital raw material.

The iron and steel industry has been largely reorganised on coastal sites in England and Wales, and on the newer iron ore deposits in eastern England, but in Scotland the industry has remained in the mid-Clyde, north Ayrshire and Falkirk areas, with greater concen-tration on a few major centres in these areas however. This allows more modern and more efficient methods of production to replace those of the many scattered furnaces which once used the local ore and fuel. Good communications with the ports are essential, and today no blast furnace is more than fifteen miles from either Glasgow or Grangemouth. Large coke ovens are now needed to process the coal, and this also favours a concentrated industry.

Production of pig iron is now confined to two large and two smaller centres. The Clyde Iron works, east of Glasgow, has three large blast furnaces, and these are efficiently linked with the Clydebridge steelworks across the river, forming an integrated iron and steel plant – hot metal being delivered from blast furnace to steel furnace with a great saving in fuel. Motherwell – synonymous in Scotland with 'steel' – has more recently acquired a similar but even larger integrated works, with three very big blast furnaces at Ravenscraig. These supply the steel furnaces there which in turn feed the new strip mills referred to below. Coatbridge has one large modern

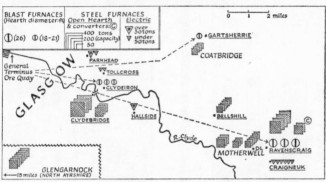

FIG. 32 Iron and Steel Industry: Centres of Production 1964*

blast furnace supplying nearby steel works and a wider market beyond. Falkirk's older and smaller furnaces supply, in particular, the demands of the iron castings industry in that area.

Normally Scotland uses only an insignificant amount of English ore, the low metallic content of which adds to fuel and transport costs per ton of pig iron. In the past there has been some dependence on England for coking coal, but in recent years production in Scotland has met all the needs of the coke ovens.

Coal is used in making steel as well as in making iron and the two sides of the industry have needed between $1\frac{1}{2}$ and $2\frac{1}{2}$ million tons every year recently. Coal used for making coke now weighs less than the ore which it is to smelt, and the total needs of the industry have been reduced by the use of oxygen in the furnaces, as well as by oil-firing of steel furnaces.

*No production at Falkirk at this time.

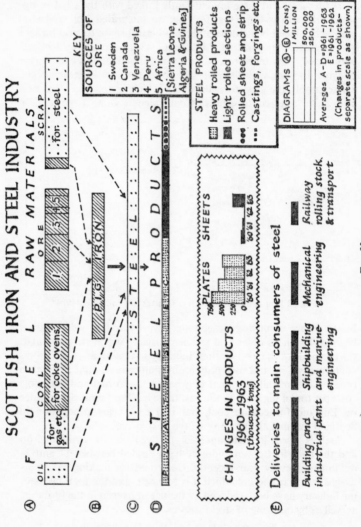

SCOTTISH IRON AND STEEL INDUSTRY

FIG. 33

Steel. Although there are several ways of making steel, in Scotland by far the largest production is in the form of ingots and most is made by the open hearth process. This is a method by which the waste heat from the furnace is used to heat the air needed for combustion, and it enables large quantities of scrap to be used. In Scotland the amount of scrap used per ton of crude steel is 30 per cent higher than that for the U.K. as a whole. (In pig iron production, the proportion is more than twice that of the U.K. so steel is doubly dependent on scrap supplies.)

There is a number of smaller furnaces, mostly of electric type, and though the total tonnage of steel from these furnaces is small it is very valuable for special purposes: castings, alloy steels and special carbon steels. As stated, most steel is made in ingots, which are rolled into plates, rails and other products, or used for forging: a smaller amount is made into castings for such things as locomotive wheel centres and axle boxes. Scotland has traditionally taken a rather greater interest in castings than other British regions.

The production of steel is concentrated in the west of the Central Lowlands, and in particular in the Clyde valley between Motherwell and Glasgow. Glengarnock, the third largest steel producing centre, is outside this main area; Coatbridge and Falkirk are at some distance from the river Clyde; but the greatest centres of Clydebridge and Motherwell are in direct rail communication with the large, modern installations at General Terminus Quay in Glasgow where ore is rapidly unloaded, and with the older Rothesay Dock near Clydebank. The main routeway of the Clyde valley also carries vast supplies of scrap.

About four-fifths of the steel produced in Scotland is used at home – mainly by the shipbuilding, constructional and other engineering industries – while about one-fifth is exported. But between the production of crude iron and steel and the finished products which reach the shipyards, factories and docks (as plates, bars, rails, castings, etc.), there are the processes of rolling, forging and other finishing operations. Much of this is done in the same works as those making the ingots of crude steel, but there are in addition a number of smaller works which carry out secondary rolling operations, using semi-finished steel as their raw material. These firms and those specialising in the production of steel castings are much more widely dispersed in the Central Lowlands, but Lanarkshire and Glasgow are still of first importance.

Developments in the steel making capacity of the Clyde area are aimed at the new market for steel strip and light plates (for car bodies etc.) as well as the modernisation of production for older markets (especially plates for shipbuilding). For the former, an immense hot-strip mill at Ravenscraig has been linked with the cold-rolling mill at Gartcosh.* This wide strip mill is backed by the new blast furnaces referred to above and by new converters which use high-velocity oxygen in the steel making process. The older markets have been given an improved capacity and quality in plate rolling by a 'four-high' plate mill at Clydebridge (the uppermost and lowest rollers giving greater strength and therefore more accuracy to the rolling process).

Both the newer and the older engineering industries benefit from new installations at Hallside and at Parkhead (including large electric-arc furnaces and other equipment for making alloy-steels and heavy castings and forgings), and, although the developments described above help to diversify the products of Scottish steel, heavy engineering remains its most important consumer. This is especially true in the Clyde area, and the production of finished steel shows this special interest of Scottish industry (Fig. 33). Though the rolling of heavy plates remains a dominant part of steel processing (linked with shipbuilding) in the west, the east Central Lowlands have a greater interest in castings – both in iron and steel. The iron casting industry of the Falkirk area has already been mentioned, and at Bathgate and Armadale there are important foundries for steel casting

The iron and steel industry of Scotland is once more adapting production to demand. As the needs of shipbuilders have declined, those of the constructional engineers (for buildings, bridges and roads) have increased, and new markets have arisen in the wider field of consumer industries, from cars to computers. The keynote is that of a greater range and quality in the steel offered to the home and foreign markets.

THE SHIPBUILDING INDUSTRY

Shipbuilding is an industry of exceptional importance to the United Kingdom, and this is not surprising when we consider the

*Near Coatbridge.

advantages of the coastal coalfields, deep tidal estuaries and long traditions of maritime trade and naval power. Britain's early industrialisation and her pioneer development of world trade gave a great impetus to shipbuilding in the nineteenth century, and although the United Kingdom has lost its previous pre-eminence, it still holds a major place among the shipbuilding nations. Britain as a whole has suffered from competition with other countries, especially Japan, and makes a contribution to world launchings only half that of ten years ago, but Scotland has at least maintained

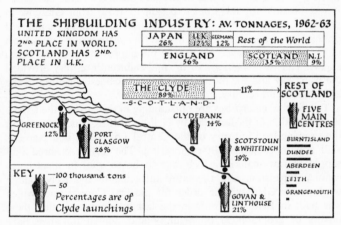

FIG. 34

its share of the nation's tonnage – a share rather more than a third of the British total. The factors which have been mentioned above – heavy industries based on coastal coalfields, with penetrating estuaries – are more applicable to the Central Lowlands of Scotland than to any other part of Britain, and it is in the Central Lowlands that 98 per cent. of Scottish ships are built. (As in the distribution of industry as a whole, and that of population too, but to a more marked degree, the west Central Lowlands stand out as a single concentrated centre; the east has a smaller total and a more scattered pattern.)

The geographical factors, by themselves, do not explain the development of the industry, although they made this development

possible. Recent history and the enterprise of great men give a
deeper understanding of the industry's growth and location. Within
the Central Lowlands the Clyde stands as the supreme estuary for
shipbuilding, yet it was this waterway which required most effort by
engineers to make its navigation possible. The twisting stream of
the mid-eighteenth century was blocked by shallows and shoals, and
the demand for its improvement came not from shipbuilders but
from the merchants who sought a tradeway. Thus Glasgow, the
port, was parent to the Clyde, the shipbuilding estuary. After the
work of John Golborne and others had made the Clyde navigable,
it was possible for the *Comet* to sail, in 1812, from Glasgow to
Greenock. This was the first steamship to be profitably employed
on this side of the Atlantic, but almost fifty years earlier James Watt
of Greenock had played his part in the improvement of the steam
engine. Thus two engineers of the mid-eighteenth century provided
the waterway and the motive power which came to fruition in the
early nineteenth century.

Two further enterprises are outstanding in the story of the Clyde:
the adaptation of the hot-blast by Neilson in 1828, which spurred on
the growing iron industry of the Central Lowlands; and Napier's
skill and thoroughness in engineering. The former ensured that
supply of raw material which was to be so vital in nineteenth-
century expansion, and the latter attracted to the Kelvinhaugh
works, near Glasgow, the order for the first Cunard liner which
was built in 1840. It is only in the last hundred years that these
factors of geographical opportunity and human initiative have
culminated in the industry as we think of it today.

Until the mid-nineteenth century, the building of the hulls was
of less importance than the making of marine engines, but after this
half century, spanning the *Comet* and the *Britannia*, as iron replaced
wood in the construction of ships, the engineers became the shipbuilders, and the industry may be said to have come of age. In the
decisive association of the Clyde and the Cunard Line, not only
Napier's engineering skill, but also the resources and resourcefulness
of Glasgow businessmen must be remembered for the capital they
found to build the *Britannia*. Thus the deepening of the Clyde
contributed twice to the shipbuilding industry: directly in making a
navigable waterway for launching boats, and indirectly in making
a trading city with the wealth to support new enterprises.

In a third way the rise of Glasgow as a great port nurtured the infant shipbuilding industry; for this industry is one of assembly, and the two basic needs of iron (later steel) and of marine engineering give us only the hull and motive power, leaving a multitude of smaller industries, which world trade encouraged in Glasgow, to supply endless fittings and furnishings. In fact, for every worker employed in a shipyard two others are employed in supplying materials for ship construction. Some of these contributory industries are branches of engineering too, such as boiler making, but many are of more varied nature, e.g. carpets, furniture, paint. Today the lighter metals and plastics have become increasingly important in the fitting out and furnishing of vessels.

The close association between the heavy iron and steel industry of the Clyde valley and the shipbuilding of Clydeside is thus supplemented by many smaller links with a wide range of industry. For a 9,000 ton vessel, about 2,250 tons of steel are needed in the shipyard, and must be delivered soon after the decision to build has been taken. Thus any shortage of steel, or delay in its supply, restricts shipbuilding, and could completely cripple it. On the other hand, any falling off in the demand for ships will be reflected in the heavy and light industries in the region. This happened between the two world wars and was a major reason for the reorganisation of the iron and steel industry, and for the encouragement of many small industries on the Industrial Estates which would be less dependent on other industries.

In meeting the demands for home and foreign shipping, the industry must cater for many special needs and keep up-to-date. While the Clyde, as a whole, makes a wide variety of craft, some yards specialise in particular types. Oil tankers have been a very important feature in shipbuilding in recent years, the trend being one of mammoth vessels built in the largest yards (taking the place of the large naval vessels which occupied so many men in pre-war shipbuilding). These tankers make great demands for steel but less for the industries which fit out and furnish passenger boats. Oil tankers are not the only boats built for special cargoes however: meat, fruit and other goods call for refrigerated ships; ore, sugar and even motor cars create their own specification for the shipbuilders. At the same time, new methods of processing and assembly (including welding where rivetting was once the rule, and prefabrication techniques) are being increasingly adopted; shipyards are being rebuilt or reorganised; and changes in engineering practice, such as those of importance in constructing ships' engines, are incorporated.

Methods of propulsion have changed greatly in the last few decades: the diesel engine has become as important as – or even more important than – the steam engine, but the latter, in the modern turbine form, has evolved far beyond the dreams of Bell or Napier.

Despite innovations in techniques, improved standards of steel and other raw materials of the industry, and such new facilities as the large dry dock at Greenock, some shipyards are not able to continue in production. At Dumbarton, despite the development there of such advanced features as the stabiliser, the yards have now closed. Some firms have been amalgamated in order to rationalise production, and some have taken on other constructional enterprises alongside the traditional one of shipbuilding, e.g. the assembly of fabricated units of the Forth Road Bridge, the making of mobile housing, and the construction of piers for North Sea oil operations.

THE TEXTILE INDUSTRY

There are four marked characteristics of Scottish textile manufacturing:

(1) its wide distribution, which makes it an industry of some importance in all regions of Scotland, with little or no concentration on the coalfields of the Central Lowlands;

(2) its wide variety of product and process, almost every type of textile being represented;

(3) the importance of high quality and of specialisation in each of the many branches of the industry;

(4) the importance of historical factors and associations which remain very strongly reflected in regional characteristics.

These features are closely related. Because of traditional skill and knowledge being vested in many relatively small firms, the products have a high value compared with mass-produced textiles in the highly concentrated coalfield regions of northern England. Location of factories is more often dependent on the pre-industrial assets of water-power and local raw materials. Although many of these factories have been completely modernised (some of them since the last war), the total value of all textiles is less than a tenth of that of the United Kingdom, and the value per worker is lower than the average, probably because of the smaller units and less mechanised methods of production than in England. However, for some of the textiles this total value is misleading: in lace making and cotton spinning the output per worker is higher, and in jute, carpets, linen, lace, rope, twine, and net, much more than one-tenth of the United Kingdom's production comes from Scotland.

Although the textile industry is not concentrated on the coalfields of the Central Lowlands as the heavy industries are, the greatest variety of textiles is found throughout these lowlands, while the Highlands and Islands, and the Southern Uplands are almost exclusively concerned with the tweed and knitwear branches of the woollen industry. Ayrshire, in particular, shows this Scottish characteristic of wide variety in textile manufacture: knitwear and hosiery (including nylon), carpets, lace, linen, and cotton are all represented. Fife is less the kingdom of linen than it once was, and the stronghold of Dunfermline is giving way: cotton, rayon and other new fibres increase in importance (today, more cotton than linen is woven there).

This increasingly wide range of textile manufactures has meant some decrease, since the last war, in Scotland's specialisation on a few textiles: cotton, the giant of world textile fibres, has been dwarfed by wool, linen and jute in Scotland since the mid-nineteenth century, but recently cotton (and some newer fibres), have grown in importance, while jute, and some types of wool and linen goods have lost ground. Nevertheless, specialisation in high quality products continues within this wider range of fibres and fabrics.

Arbroath may be taken as an example of the industrial inertia which has been referred to in the location of factories. Flax and hemp had to be imported from Russia after local cultivation had failed to supply the growing demand of the spinning mills in the early nineteenth century. But the advantage of siting the mills near water, together with the accumulated skill and capital, have ensured a continued concentration of the industry, although water power, like the local supplies of fibre, failed to meet modern requirements. Thus we find five firms now processing flax as well as a wide range of other fibres – natural and synthetic – and manufacturing such goods as sail-canvas, sacks, filter-cloth, cord and twine.

Wool. The historical factors in location of mills has been matched to some extent by the persistence of traditional fibres and traditional processes. This is most true of the Highlands and Islands, where Harris Tweed and Shetland knitwear industries still flourish. To gain the official stamp, Harris Tweed must be made from pure virgin Scottish wool, spun in the Outer Hebrides, and woven by the

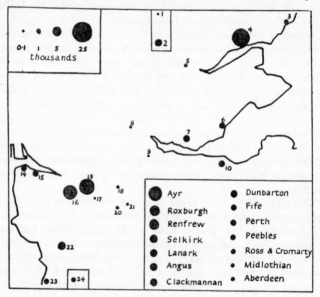

FIG. 35 The textile industry. Employment in the industry is shown in 21 towns, accounting for nearly 60 per cent of all textile workers. Other centres are shown by county symbols (nearly 40 per cent).

Key to towns: 1. Inverness; 2. Aberdeen; 3. Arbroath; 4. Dundee; 5. Perth; 6. Kirkcaldy; 7. Dunfermline; 8. Stirling; 9. Falkirk; 10. Edinburgh; 11. Dumbarton; 12. Clydebank; 13. Glasgow; 14. Greenock; 15. Port Glasgow; 16. Paisley; 17. Rutherglen; 18. Coatbridge; 19. Airdrie; 20. Hamilton; 21. Motherwell and Wishaw; 22. Kilmarnock; 23. Ayr; 24. Dumfries

islanders in their own homes. Most wool is imported from the mainland, and most spinning is carried out by large firms in Stornoway, who distribute the yarn to hundreds of weavers scattered throughout the island. Much of the tweed made in the Western Isles is exported: in 1963, three-quarters was sold abroad. This industry has preserved the economy of the 'Long Island', despite the difficulties of crofting and fishing. In the Shetland Isles, it is a combination of local skill, traditions in pattern and colour, and the quality of the wool from the native sheep which has maintained the knitting industry. Thousands of Shetland knitters, some using hand-operated machines, contribute both to the prosperity of their island and to the reputation of Scottish textiles.

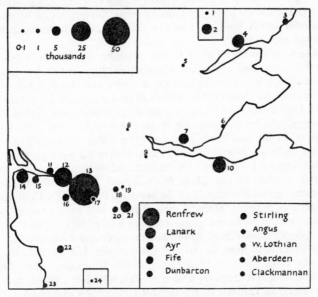

FIG. 36 The engineering industry (engineering, shipbuilding and electrical goods). Employment is shown in 24 towns, accounting for 75 per cent of all engineering workers. Other centres of employment are shown by county symbols (nearly 25 per cent). For key to towns, see legend to Fig. 35, opposite.

In the Borders, tweeds and knitwear are more closely located in the Tweed basin, with a few outposts such as Dumfries. A further contrast with woollen manufacturing in the Islands is that imported wool has long had precedence over the native fibre. From the making of long woollen stockings in the later eighteenth century, Hawick has successfully turned to knitted underwear and fully fashioned outerwear, while Galashiels has continued to weave tweed of high quality. Other nearby centres share in these two branches of the Border woollen industry.

But woollens are not limited to the extreme west, north, and south-east of Scotland. From Aberdeen to Edinburgh in the east, and in Glasgow, Lanarkshire, and Ayrshire in the west, there are many small factories making hosiery, knitwear, tweed, and blankets among other woollen goods, usually highly specialised, e.g. Alloa and Greenock are noted for knitting yarns, Stewarton and Kilmarnock for tartan bonnets, while in the east many factories make knitted gloves.

Linen. While the Highlands and Southern Uplands have traditionally encouraged woollen manufacture, the Central Lowlands have always had a strong interest in linen, and this is the textile which may be considered as a basis of past prosperity (comparable with English woollens). Flax was grown in almost every part of the country, and by the sixteenth century it was the most important export. In the next three centuries other fibres displaced flax for many purposes. Jute in the east, and cotton in the west, grew up as substitutes for linen: they were cheaper, and were encouraged by the better supplies of raw fibres from abroad. But the demand for fine linen goods has stimulated the import of flax from the Continent (especially Belgium, Holland, and Russia), and from England, so that Scotland continues to manufacture a large part of the United Kingdom's linen fabric. Kilbirnie (Ayrshire) and Johnstone (Renfrewshire) have linen thread and net factories, but the industry is mostly to be found in Fife, Angus, Perth, Kincardine, and Aberdeenshire, and it caters for a wide market: from heavy sail cloth and tarpaulins in Dundee, to the lightest fabrics such as damask table cloths at Dunfermline. Mixtures of linen and cotton, such as 'union' goods (which have linen weft and cotton warp), are made at Kirkcaldy, and flax yarn is woven with rayon, silk and nylon at Dunfermline. The industry has survived on its reputation for quality, and the pioneering of machine embroidery at Dunfermline was important in establishing this reputation.

Jute. Jute quickly gained supremacy over flax and hemp for coarse fabric (such as sacking), when a method of processing was found in the mid-nineteenth century. This processing involved the use of whale oil, and Dundee was, at this time, an important whaling port. Although the industry has declined in output in this century

Dundee remains the outstanding centre of production and, as with other textiles, specialisation has enabled it to flourish. India makes cheaper standard goods, and these are imported into the United Kingdom. Almost all the spinning of yarn, and two-thirds of weaving and bag sewing, is carried out in Dundee, when the British industry is fully employed. All the raw fibre comes from East Pakistan, and, using the most modern machinery in the world, yarn

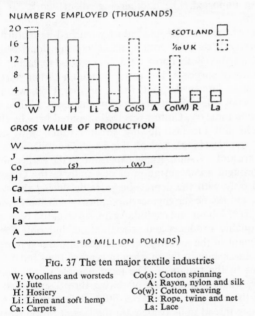

FIG. 37 The ten major textile industries

W: Woollens and worsteds
J: Jute
H: Hosiery
Li: Linen and soft hemp
Ca: Carpets

Co(s): Cotton spinning
A: Rayon, nylon and silk
Co(w): Cotton weaving
R: Rope, twine and net
La: Lace

is produced for carpets, cables, and ropes, and is woven into bags, packing cloth, backing for linoleum, and a host of other purposes.

Two textile industries provide us with almost all out floor covering in the manufacture of carpets and linoleum. Wool is the main fibre used in carpet manufacture, which has developed in Scotland from an early cottage industry, and now contributes almost a third of Britain's output. The largest factories are in Glasgow and Kilmarnock. Jute has a threefold use in floor covering: as an important element in the making of woollen carpets; in the production of all-jute carpets (in which Scotland is responsible for all Britain's output); and in the making of linoleum (in which Scotland is the leading Commonwealth country). While the west of Scotland is more concerned with carpet manufacture, it is in Fife and Angus, and especially in Kirkcaldy, that linoleum is made. Linen preceded jute as the fibre for 'floorcloth', but linseed oil is the essential element contributed by the flax plant today, giving linoleum its name, and being imported, like another ingredient – cork – at the east coast ports.

Cotton. At the time the jute industry reached its maturity in the later nineteenth century, cotton manufacturing flourished in and around Glasgow. Both fibres were newcomers, replacing flax and wool for many purposes. But cotton made an earlier start in west Scotland than jute in the east, for soon after 1750, when textiles played a major role in Scottish economy, there was a home spinning and weaving industry. Cotton was well favoured here by the damp atmosphere and the fast flowing streams (often with adjoining meadows for bleaching), and on this basis new mills were built in Lanarkshire and Ayrshire. Rapid expansion in the earlier nineteenth century brought a concentration of new mills to the Glasgow district, and only with the depression in trade during the American Civil War did the newer engineering industry rob the Clyde valley cotton mills of labour and capital. Again, survival has been achieved by high quality products and specialisation, but only for a very small remnant of the industry, since Lancashire was a more potent rival to Lanarkshire in the nineteenth century than India has been to Dundee in the twentieth. The most notable survival has been in Paisley, where manufacture of sewing thread succeeded that of shawls as the major industry. Four-fifths of the output is exported from Paisley thread mills (which are the largest in the world), and other mills at Neilston and elsewhere in Renfrewshire.

Availability of fibre from India aided the development of cotton manufacture as it did those of jute. In many ways, therefore, Paisley and Dundee represent comparable textile developments, both in the change-over from linen to other fibres, and in the great concentration of their respective industries in these two centres.

But Glasgow itself has not lost all interest in cotton manufacture. Just as cotton thread manufacture developed in Paisley from an earlier linen thread industry, so the present cotton goods produced in Glasgow are successors to the fine linens made for export to the Continent in the eighteenth century, and are thus high quality fabrics such as ginghams, poplins, and voiles.

Outwith Lanarkshire and Renfrewshire (where over 100 factories existed even in 1900), Catrine in Ayrshire is a notable centre for cotton manufacture, not only because it now carries through every process in a modernised factory, but also because its isolation, as the only cotton works in the county, is an example of that dispersed pattern in textiles to which Dundee and Paisley are outstanding exceptions.

The principle of specialisation ensuring survival when mass-production threatens an old industry is shown in the history of the Irvine valley in Ayrshire. Here, in the Darvel-Newmilns-Galston area, about two-thirds of British lace is made, the industry having arisen in the later nineteenth century when hand-loom weaving declined.

Wool and flax from the farms, water and power from the rivers, all have played their part in the origins of Scottish textiles; but maritime traditions have also been significant. Apart from overseas trade, which has always been vital to the industry, the ports and shipping create their own demand for canvas, rope, and nets. All these are more important manufactures in Scotland than in Britain generally. Canvas and rope are made at many ports such as Dundee, Aberdeen, Arbroath, Port Glasgow and Greenock, while fishing nets are woven at Kilbirnie, Musselburgh and Greenock.

The textile industry has turned from home produced fibres to imported wool, flax, jute, and cotton; but it has also developed some of the new synthetic fibres. Rayon yarn is produced at east coast textile towns (Dundee, Arbroath and Montrose), and at Motherwell and Cumnock in the west. The manufacture of nylon yarn is centred mainly in Lanarkshire and Ayrshire.

In the seventeenth century, textiles were, together with the food surplus of both land and sea, the principal exports of Scotland. The hand-knitted stockings of the North-east, the heavy grey cloth of the Borders, and colourful plaidings from the west country, were sold throughout western Europe. From this trade has grown the present world-wide export of Scottish knitwear, tweeds, fine cotton and lace goods, carpets, ropes, nets, and many other products. Although in some ways dwarfed by heavy industry, the manufacture of textiles is as vital as ever to Scottish prosperity and Britain's trade.

X · POPULATION

FEW countries have a more unevenly distributed population than Scotland. Of the 5 million people, 4 million live in the Central Lowlands. Concentration of population is not only a reflection of lowland and highland environments, however. The map overleaf shows towns and larger villages by dots of comparative sizes, and the scattered rural population by county 'stars'. The dots show actual location; the stars represent the total in each county of all the small, dispersed settlements of less than one thousand people. Not only the concentration in the Central Lowlands should be noted, but also the general pattern of coast and river settlements. The lands bordering the estuaries of the rivers Clyde, Forth, and Tay, the hinterland of these estuaries (especially of the Clyde), are mostly densely populated in urban 'clusters'. Only the more isolated, but still relatively important, north-east coast region has an appreciable urban population outwith the Central Lowlands. Almost all the towns and large villages are below 800 feet, and almost all of them are within 20 miles of the coast. The exceptions are limited to a few settlements in the higher valleys (mainly of rivers Tweed and Clyde).

Concentration of population is not simply related to lowland and coastal access. The previous chapters have indicated other factors, such as distribution of mineral wealth. But the major contrast of the three regions is apparent. Renfrewshire has over 1,400 people per square mile; Sutherland has less than 7. These average densities conceal many differences. The most significant, perhaps, is the difference between the few people who still live isolated lives in the country and the many who live in large towns. The sixteen largest burghs, ranging from Glasgow with 1,090,000* people downward, account for almost exactly half of Scotland's population. In the sketch-map these are shown to be even more closely linked to coastal lowlands than is the population as a whole, for only Aberdeen lies outwith the Central Lowlands and only the Clyde valley 'cluster' is more than 10 miles from open water.

The very great concentration of people in a few settlements is emphasised by considering the urban fraction of Scotland's population

*1951.

in 1901 and 1951, viz. 74 per cent and 83 per cent respectively. This increase of urban population was both absolute and relative. Almost a million more people now live in the centres of 1,000 or more inhabitants while total population has increased by only half a million. All three zones of Scotland have shared this relative growth of urban population though it is naturally most marked in the Central Lowlands. Only in the Highlands is the growth of urban population at a lower rate than the national increase of total population. The following table shows a division of Scotland based on county boundaries approximating to the physical regions. The

	Percentage Urban Population in 1951	Percentage Increase in Urban Population 1901-1951
Scotland	82·9	27·2
Central industrial region . .	91·8	33
Northern counties . . .	62·1	8·4
Southern counties . . .	52	12·7

most highly urbanised counties are Lanark (96·6 per cent in urban areas), Renfrew (95·2 per cent), and Midlothian (95 per cent) while the most rural are Sutherland (7·9 per cent), Ross and Cromarty (18·9 per cent) and Berwick (27·1 per cent).

Not only have the Highlands and Islands lost much of their rural population; in the Central Lowlands and Southern Uplands the drift to the towns has been considerable. The movement from country to town areas has been regional to some extent, e.g. Edinburgh has drawn people from the Borders and east coast while Glasgow has drawn more from the western counties. But the overall effect has been that of a huge magnet – the Central Lowlands – attracting population from every corner of Scotland. Some have moved beyond the homeland and in return other countries have contributed to Scotland's population, but this exchange is mostly a loss from the countryside and a gain for the towns. The northern counties have lost about 58 per cent of their population by migration since 1871, the southern counties have lost about 55 per cent in this time. Even in Central Scotland, migration reduces the rate of growth of population; in the west about one-quarter and in the east about one-third of the population has been lost by migration since 1871.

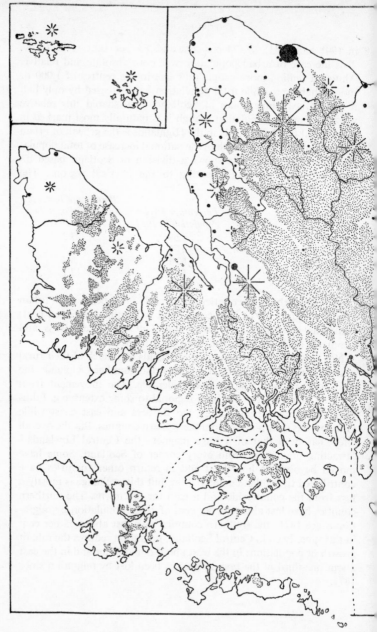

Fig. 38

The rural populat

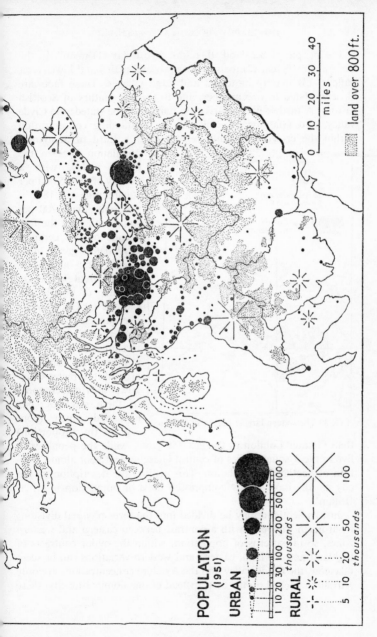

POPULATION
(1951)

URBAN

1 10 20 30 100 200 500 1000
thousands

RURAL

5 10 20 50 100
thousands

0 10 20 30 40
miles

land over 800ft.

shown by counties

FIG. 38

The people of Scotland, therefore, live today (1) mainly in the Central Lowlands; (2) mainly in the coastal plains and lower river valleys; (3) mainly in towns and large villages. These facts are closely related to one another, and to the last century of Scottish history. A further particularisation remains to be stated: the Clyde valley, and Glasgow especially, is an outstanding concentration within the crowded lowland region. Over a third of Scotland's population lives in the Clyde valley, with a density of over 5,000 per square mile (in 1801 it was only about 700 per square mile). In the first decade of this century, Clydebank grew more quickly than any other town in Great Britain. On the map of population, the 'dot' for Glasgow has over-lapped neighbouring settlements. In fact, it resembles a 'sun' with a number of 'satellites' around it. Greater Glasgow, which includes some of these satellites, has expanded much more rapidly (in proportion)

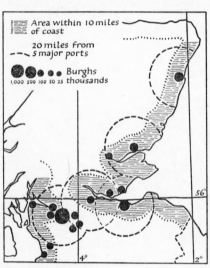

FIG. 39 The sixteen largest burghs of Scotland

than Greater London in the last 150 years, while the people who live in the 3 square miles of central Glasgow represent almost one-fifth of Scotland's population. This justifies the description of the city as 'the most highly compressed mass of population in Great Britain'.

Just as Scotland may be divided into the three physical divisions from north to south, with a contrast between eastern and western zones, so in patterns of population, within the major contrasts of highland and lowland, eastern and western variations can be seen. Glasgow, the Clyde valley and the Ayrshire concentrations are only partially matched on the east. Instead of one dominating city, there are three large burghs and, apart from its historical and adminis-trative significance, Edinburgh does not dominate the pattern of settlement as Glasgow does in the west. Similarly, the location of medium and smaller towns makes a more dispersed pattern and the importance of rural population is shown by the map to be greater in the eastern counties.

It is necessary to refer, finally, to future possibilities. The future may produce changes of distribution of population more slowly than those of the past 150 years but more likely to last because of that and because they will result from present planning for future needs. Such plans aim to weaken the greatest concentrations such as Glasgow itself, and to favour a more balanced distribution in smaller communities.

Population Changes: 1951-1961. Although Scotland's population has increased by over 80,000 in this period, this represents less than a third of the rate of growth between 1931 and 1951. While the birthrate has risen since 1953, the net loss by migration (more than a quarter of a million persons) has also risen. It is estimated that about half the emigrants went to other parts of the United Kingdom and half overseas.

Of the four cities, Glasgow's loss more than outweighs the gains of the other three. But the Central Clydeside Conurbation has con-tinued to grow, and the urban population as a whole (cities and burghs) has remained almost as preponderant a proportion of the population (about 70 per cent). The 'industrial belt' now has over 76 per cent of the population (just one per cent more than in 1951) while the crofting counties have lost nearly 3 per cent, and the Border Counties over 6 per cent.

Of the individual counties, Bute suffered the most severe rate of decrease, and Caithness gained at the highest rate. The New Towns and, at a lesser rate, some of the burghs grew rapidly in the inter-censal period, as shown below:

New Towns					1951	1961
Glenrothes	.	.	.	.	1,682	12,746
East Kilbride	.	.	.	.	5,136	31,972
Cumbernauld	.	.	.	.	2,927	4,924
Totals					9,745	49,642

7

Burghs (increase of 20 per cent or more)

	1951	1961
Thurso	3,249	8,038
Dollar	1,389	1,955
Bearsden	12,264	17,022
Haddington	4,498	5,506
Grangemouth	15,432	18,860
Kirkintilloch	15,117	18,257
Annan	4,631	5,572

XI · COMMUNICATIONS AND TRADE

COMMUNICATIONS

COMMUNICATIONS express the human reactions to the physical environment in a pattern of routes and route centres. The constant factors of relief, drainage and climate are seen in operation, in the past and present, throughout the changing human scene: economic, strategic, and cultural. In Scotland, as elsewhere, the geography of a nation may be seen in historical perspective through that network of roads and railways, and of sea and air links, which focus on bridge sites, defensive strongholds, market towns, ports, and great centres of mining and manufacturing.

The shape of Scotland has a compelling influence on man's attempts at intercommunication. Its elongation, north to south, demands the strongest lines in this direction to link the Uplands, Lowlands, and Highlands. The great firths, which break the coastline, disturb also the continuity of these linear routes, and give strength to the shorter, transverse lines, especially in the Lowlands. The relief and drainage also hinder rather than help the north-south routes on land, but, while this is strongly accented in the Highlands, there are very notable exceptions in the south of Scotland.

Road and rail. The contrast of the three regions in communications is partly a result of relief, and partly of the differences in distribution of population. The Southern Uplands, with its coastal and valley lowlands, is characterised by a strong but open pattern of roads and railways, trending north and south. It follows from the borderland position of this region, that routes have been of great strategic importance in the past, and that they have been strongly forged links, in the modern industrial age, between the prosperous lowlands on either side of the Border. It is a region of through-routes. In contrast, the Central Lowlands is distinct in the density of routes, which matches the density of population, and utilises the wider river lowlands. It has the strongest east-west component of any part of Scotland's communications, and is, as a whole, the central 'knot' which ties together all Scottish routes.

On the other hand, the Highlands is noted for its weakness in offering opportunities for communications, and here relief is most dominant in guiding roads and railways by the broad straths,

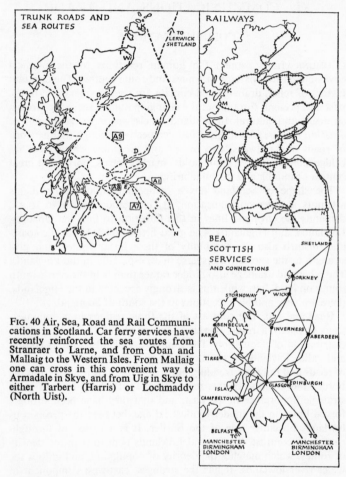

FIG. 40 Air, Sea, Road and Rail Communications in Scotland. Car ferry services have recently reinforced the sea routes from Stranraer to Larne, and from Oban and Mallaig to the Western Isles. From Mallaig one can cross in this convenient way to Armadale in Skye, and from Uig in Skye to either Tarbert (Harris) or Lochmaddy (North Uist).

straightened and deepened by ice, so that a few main routes are encased between the mountain walls, seeking a low pass to the next valley, and rarely able to branch into side-routes. Apart from the limits set by relief, there are serious difficulties in the Highlands which are caused by climate (heavy and persistent snow cover in some areas; extreme rainfall and frost-action contributing to instability of foundations and to landslides). In most Highland valleys, routes are constrained not only by altitude and slope but usually by loch and marsh on the lower levels also. The more scattered population does not encourage the building of roads and railways, and those communities which do exist far to the north and west are very isolated. Whereas, in the Lowlands, alternative routes and route centres compete for traffic and trade, the Highlands and Southern Uplands present much less choice in communications, both in direction taken and mode of transport (road, rail and water tend to be complementary rather than competitive.)

As in other geographical features of Scotland, communications show the contrast between east and west, as well as the broad variations of the three major regions already considered. The east is a land of coastal access, while the west has relatively few coastal plains of sufficient continuity to provide major routes. Road and railway are often sited on the raised beaches of both east and west coasts, but this is true for greater distances in the east, e.g. between Inverness and Caithness.

This contrast is well marked in the Highlands (where the east coast plains are sometimes narrow but almost everywhere accessible), but in the south of Scotland, too, the eastern coastal route contrasts with the western valley routes (especially that of river Annan and river Clyde), which avoid the circuitous coast of Galloway. Thus the great route-centre of Glasgow is a valley settlement, sited at a river crossing, with a radial pattern of communications: Edinburgh is a strategic stronghold of the coastal plain with its main east-west routes following the alignment of the Firth of Forth, and with relatively weak routes to north and south. Dundee and Aberdeen also have route patterns of coastal type, although the rivers Dee and Don are essential factors in the siting of Aberdeen.

The contrast of east and west is most striking in the communications of northern Scotland, where the strong north-south route of the east coast forms a base-line from which the west Highlands derive transverse links. Thus from Dingwall both road and rail reach out to the Kyle of Lochalsh, and a road to Ullapool, both routes making use of physical features derived from river capture and ice action. Lairg, further north, is a route centre for an extensive area of the Highlands, while Inverness to the south is strongly linked to Fort William and the Kyle of Lochalsh on the west, and by the Strath Spey route to the central Grampian region.

The east coast railway route has had for many years the advantage over the road by the bridging of Forth and Tay, but the Forth Road Bridge at Queensferry and the road bridge over the Tay at Dundee will now greatly strengthen the routes of the east Central Lowlands; and better access by road will stimulate industry north of the Lothians. The circuitous route via the Kincardine road bridge, and the delays caused by ferries over the two Firths will no longer hamper the development of Fife and Angus, though the individual character of these counties may change in the process of closer assimilation and the growth of arterial functions north of Edinburgh. The older bridge-points at Stirling and Perth remain important for they attract traffic which converges at the gaps between Campsie Fells, Ochil Hills and Sidlaw Hills. From these gap towns, valley routes reach into the Highlands. From Perth the Tay-Garry route penetrates the Grampians, using the passes at Killiecrankie and Drumochter, to reach Strath Spey. From Stirling the West Highlands are approached via Callendar and Glen Ogle.

Only one major land route of the Highlands does not stem from the eastern coastal plains: that from Glasgow north to Fort William. This route is not favoured, as are those of the east, by coastal access or economic demand and the bridging of the Clyde remains a function of Glasgow. Here, as at Stirling and Perth, routes are focussed in a radial pattern, and congestion of traffic has long been a severe problem. The Whiteinch tunnel has recently been added to facilities of bridges and ferries, but the larger solution to Glasgow's function as a route centre lies in its hinterland as well as at the centre.

The artery between Glasgow and Carlisle, A74, carries three quarters of Scotland's traffic with England and is essential to the prosperity of the Central Lowlands. Much of this has been modernised, and the reconstruction of other roads in a fully integrated network has been planned. But land routes are only one aspect of communications, and the Clyde valley is a stronger node than any other because of its land, sea and air connections.

Canals. As a country of extensive highlands, Scotland could not be expected to develop a great canal system, and in 1830 it had less than 5 per cent (by mileage) of British inland waterways. Yet the outline of Scotland offers tempting opportunities for short cuts across the many waistlines of the mainland and its peninsulas. Earth movements and the work of glaciers have conspired in this, and the Caledonian Canal between North-west Highlands and Grampians is an outstanding example of loch and valley being used to unite the Firths at either end. It was constructed by Telford, early in the nineteenth century, with government aid, for the use of coasters and fishing vessels. But there are many locks along the Caledonian Canal, and the economic potential of the region is too low to generate heavy traffic. The Crinan Canal (1800) severs the Kintyre peninsula to allow a shorter passage from the Firth of Clyde to the Hebrides, and is of value for the many 'puffers' and other small craft on the west coast routes. It was, however, in the Central Lowlands that the greatest incentive for cheap transport arose during the Industrial Revolution, and here the two great navigable waterways approach to within 30 miles. Thus the Forth-Clyde Canal, from Grangemouth to Bowling, had much in its favour. The needs of the Central Coalfield industries were also served by the Monkland Canal (Coatbridge to Glasgow) and the Union Canal (Falkirk to Edinburgh). But the convenience of road and rail transport have entirely displaced this traffic. Only the Caledonian and Crinan Canals are now in use for freight. The former accounts for over two-thirds of the net ton-mileage while the latter accounts for over two-thirds of the total number of vessels.

Coastal Waters. The coastal waters are naturally more important for Scotland's internal communications than canals, since the population has a strong coastal trend in its distribution, and the coast is an exceptionally long one, including the islands and peninsulas of the west. Thus the ports of the east are linked in a north – south pattern of coastal trade, matching the land routes, and, of greater geographical significance, the Western Isles and west coast are served by a maze of sea routes, with a more dominant east – west direction. The islanders depend on the maintenance of these passenger and freight services for their economic survival. The passenger services may be grouped into, firstly, the Firth of Clyde area (especially important for holiday makers) with its extension of routes by the land crossing at Tarbert to Islay and Jura and, secondly, the services from the four ports – Oban, Fort William, Mallaig, and

Kyle of Lochalsh–to both the Inner and Outer Hebrides. But cargo services carry to these outlying communities such a variety of goods that the boats may be described as sailing emporia. The northern isles are linked by sea to the ports of Aberdeen and Thurso (the former serving Lerwick and Kirkwall, the latter, Stromness) and so extend the range of north-south routes which characterise eastern Scotland.

External sea communications of Scotland are more fully considered below in the account of trade. But though less important than goods, passengers form part of the traffic of some Scottish ports. Services to Northern Ireland are strongest; Glasgow to Belfast; Ardrossan to Belfast and Stranraer to Larne, the shortest link between the two countries. Transatlantic liners call at Greenock but only special sailings connect Glasgow with distant lands. Modernisation of Leith as a port may in the future attract larger liners, but at present the passenger services are limited to the smaller boats crossing to Scandinavia, Belgium, the Netherlands and Iceland.

Air. The isolation of the Highlands and Islands has been dramatically reduced in the twentieth century by the aeroplane, as it was in the nineteenth century by the steamship. The Glasgow airport at Renfrew (to be replaced by Abbotsinch) maintains services to the airports of the Western Isles, while Aberdeen is the main point of departure for the Northern Isles. Charter flights, and, from Renfrew, the Air Ambulance service for the Western Isles, augment the regular flights operated by British European Airways and other services.

The external air communications of Scotland are centred on Prestwick, three miles north of Ayr, which has an unrivalled reputation among British airports for its good weather. From Prestwick routes radiate to Europe and North America, with connections to other airports throughout the world. It is favourably placed for the crossing of the North Atlantic by the short route to Gander in Newfoundland, and for crossing the North Sea to Scandinavia, and it is close to the most densely populated region in Scotland. While passenger services are the main function of this international airport (and the tourist industry benefits from these), it is important in stimulating the world-wide trade of Scotland, for the modern commercial traveller is air-minded.

Finally we may sum up some of the problems and possibilities which geographical conditions set before us. The relative isolation of Scotland, in its British and European space-relations, has been steadily reduced by developments in transport. But many areas of the Highlands remain isolated, and the spiral of depopulation continues. Good transport alone does not revive remote villages: in fact the road which brings trade may also take the countryman to the town. Light aircraft – as used now by business executives – could do more in the future to link Highland centres with main airline services. In the areas of dense population, especially the Clyde valley, a re-organised system of road and rail services has now been inaugurated, with electrification of suburban railways in some key districts. Among the large cities and towns, Glasgow has the largest hinterland in population, and therefore most requires improvement in rapid, frequent trains and buses, while Aberdeen, with the largest hinterland in area, could most profitably be strengthened as a centre for connecting outlying settlements.

TRADE

The historical and geographical background to Scottish trade

Even before the Act of Union (1707), trade existed between Scotland and the rest of Europe. An unfriendly North Sea could give the trader a rough passage in either direction but it was a short voyage between the Continent and the east of Scotland. The estuaries of the rivers Tay and Forth and the mouth of the river Dee offered natural harbourages with some shelter. Thus commercial activities between Dundee, Leith and Aberdeen and the Low countries, Scandinavia, France and the Baltic lands date back several centuries. The west of Scotland, however, was not so favoured partly on account of its aloofness and partly because of the absence of a serviceable port. Commercial transactions between the west of Scotland and north and western Europe are on record but the natural encumbrances of the river Clyde prevented Glasgow from competing with the ports of the east coast.

In the report of Commissioner Tucker in 1651 on the revenue of Scotland there is an informative account of the state of the Clyde and of the nature of the trade at Glasgow prior to 1707: 'With the exception of its coligners (college folk), all the inhabitants are traders, some to Ireland, with small smiddy coals, in open boats from 4-10 tons, from whence they bring hoops, rings, barrel staves, meal, oats, butter; some to France with plaiding, coals, and herrings from which the return is salt, pepper, raisins, prunes; some to Norway for timber. There have likewise been some who have ventured as far as the Barbadoes but the loss which they sustained by being obliged to come home late in the year has made them discontinue going there any more. The mercantile genius of the people is strong if they were not kept under by the shallowness of their river, every day, more and more increasing and filling up so that no vessel of any burden can come up nearer the town than 14 miles where they must unload and send their timber on rafts and all other commodities by 3-4 tons at a time, in small cobbles or boats of 3, 4, 5 and none above 6 tons a boat. There are 12 vessels belonging to the merchants of the port, total 957 tons, none of which come up to the town.'

The commerce of Glasgow received its initial and superlative stimulus in the Act of Union which, ill-liked at first by some, opened up a sphere of trade for which its position was pre-eminently suited. Geographical location coupled with man-made legislation pointed the way to trading ventures at first in the New World and, in due course, in every quarter of the globe. The east of Scotland was, and is, not entirely deprived of trade with the Western world but none of its ports has attained that degree of importance to Scottish trade which Glasgow and the Clyde ports now indisputably possess.

The supremacy of the river Clyde, as a commercial channel, was not, however, achieved in a short space of time nor without a great deal of application and ingenuity. Not the least were the projects designed to render the river navigable as far up as the centre of Glasgow. From being an unpretentious river, shallow in parts and elsewhere handicapped by inches or islets of river-borne deposits, it has been converted, by a prolonged process of regularisation, deepening, and dredging, into a channel capable of permitting passage to all but the largest vessels of the world.

Permission to trade with the English dependencies, the principal advantage of the Act of Union to Scotland, began to manifest itself in the middle and late eighteenth century. Contemporaneous with the growing revolution in industry came the flow of commodities from the New World to the west of Scotland. Tobacco, of which Glasgow had for a time almost a monopoly of the trade with Europe, was followed by cotton and sugar-cane as regular and major imports into Scotland. Even now these commodities remain important in Scottish industry and are to the fore in its present trading activities.

Not by mere chance, also, did the Industrial Revolution provide the west of Scotland with further opportunities for industrial development and commercial expansion. The existence of coal and iron deposits in this area, particularly in the vicinity of Glasgow, rendered possible the expansion of the metallurgical industry of Scotland. Both were indispensable in the provision of rails and rolling stock in the railway construction period of the middle nineteenth century and in the development of the steel, engineering and ship-building activities that became increasingly important in the latter half of the same century. Today, by virtue of the export value of vehicles, machinery, and ships, these very industries give Glasgow and Scotland universal repute and yet, iron-ore, the basic raw material of the Scottish steel industry, no longer available in quantity in Scotland, is an essential import and most of it is now brought in via the Clyde.

The preponderance of industry which has become a feature of the Lower Clyde area presents a lop-sided appearance to Scottish commerce. While there is considerable trading activity in the east coast ports, import and export trade through Glasgow is of such a magnitude as to far outstrip that of each of the east ports. Such a state of affairs may not be wholly desirable but it is nevertheless inevitable as long as the essentials of industry and the basic needs of the people have to be brought, in no small part, from the Americas and as long as there are tempting demands from the same source for products made in Scotland.

The Character of Scottish Import and Export Trade

Inadequacy of data. It is difficult to obtain an accurate impression of the trading activities of Scotland as a unit and of its contribution to the trade of Great Britain as a whole. There is no statistical information available by which to measure the import and export trade of Scotland (see Catto Committee Report). Over and above the actual in-and-out traffic at Scottish ports, imports of Scotland may arrive at English ports and may, thereafter, be sent north by road, rail or coastal vessel. Similarly, not all of Scotland's exports are sent out of Scottish ports. To make up cargoes, many consignments of goods may go south to be loaded, for example, at Liverpool. It is not easy to compile an accurate account of this sort of traffic for there is no sustained or public information available. But the road and rail traffic of this sort between Scotland and England can hardly be passed over without mention.

There is also a regular exchange or flow of goods between the two countries. Though this traffic may not be regarded as 'imports' and 'exports', it is a vital part of Scottish trade. Southwards go fish, meat, meal, potatoes, whisky, textiles, machinery, vehicles, etc. Northwards come clothing, textile fibres (raw or partly finished), coal, household and electrical goods, vehicles, etc. For this sort of internal exchange there is also no public record and, without that information, it is not possible to make an estimate of its proportions. But the volume of north and south-bound traffic, in the form of heavy lorries, alone, on the main England-Scotland road over Beattock Pass, is so enormous, by night as much as by day, as to suggest that this form of exchange between Scotland and England and Wales is very important.

The paragraphs which follow refer to direct import and export trade and are based on local official reports as well as on the annual statements of trade in Great Britain.* These latter give an account of the direct import and export trade of the ports of Scotland. This source of information is also a difficult one to use for not all commodities are measured in the same unit. Their worth, it is true, is assessed in sterling values but this medium is not always the best guide to the importance of import and export trade.

The West of Scotland. The import and export activities of the west of Scotland are centred almost entirely in the Clyde area. The tonnage of imports is very great but what is as noteworthy is the immense range of commodities received. The imports of Glasgow resemble a catalogue, tremendous in length and too great to be detailed. Tea (India and Ceylon), wine (France and Spain), dairy-produce (Holland, Denmark and Australasia), fruits of many types (Caribbean, Canary Isles, South Africa, Middle East, Australasia North America), grains of many kinds and flour (Canada, Australia, South America), livestock (Ireland), meat (Argentine, Australasia),

*Annual Statement of the Trade of the United Kingdom, Vol. IV. Supplement: Imports and exports of each port. (H.M.S.O.)

these are common shipments into the Clyde for general distribution throughout Scotland.

Raw materials, in raw or semi-prepared conditions, compose another important group of imports. They are of great diversity and equally wide are their sources of origin. The principal discharges are petroleum (Caribbean, Middle East), oil-seeds (Asiatic, African and American tropical lands), rubber (Malaya), iron ore (Canada, Venezuela, Sweden, North and West Africa), paper (Canada, Scandinavia), tobacco (African colonies, Caribbean, U.S.A.), timber (West Africa, Canada, Scandinavia). Some raw cotton reaches the Clyde direct from cotton growing lands like U.S.A. and the Caribbean islands, but from sundry sources abroad come textile yarns and pieces for additional treatment and manufacture. For further industrial processing, too, come ingots or bars of aluminium, lead and zinc from America, Africa and Australia.

IMPORTS   EXPORTS

Imp. A: Food and beverages
B: Basic metals
C: Mineral fuels
D: Manufactured goods

Exp. A: Manufactured goods
B: Food, beverages and tobacco (particularly whisky)
C: Miscellaneous items

FIG. 41 Glasgow's trade

To Greenock, dwarfed in importance by nearby Glasgow, come shiploads of unrefined sugar and tobacco from the Caribbean, bananas and oilseeds from the tropics. Loads of timber and iron ore as well as crude and refined oil are brought to Ardrossan.

Exports from the west of Scotland to places outside Great Britain are likewise exclusively from the Clyde. Important as they are to Greenock, the exports of its ships, refined syrup and sugar are again completely eclipsed by the gigantic cargoes from Glasgow. This outlet is the main one for goods made all over Scotland. Heading the list of exports are Scotch whisky and iron and steel goods – ships, steel plates and tubes, boilers, cast iron goods, cars and car parts and machinery. A great trade is done in textile goods like carpets from Glasgow itself, jute bags and pieces from Dundee, lace from Ayrshire, tartan materials, tweeds, and knitwear from the Borders. Biscuits and beer from Glasgow, Edinburgh or Alloa linoleum from Kirkcaldy, stoves and cookers from Falkirk, sewing machines from Clydebank, cotton thread from Paisley, chemicals from Grangemouth, and an endless miscellany of light goods assembled and packed at the various Scottish Industrial Estates – all are sent as on a conveyor belt, along roads and railways focusing on Glasgow from which they go to buyers all over the world.

'General cargo', so frequently used to refer to transhipments from the Clyde area, is appropriate enough. It illustrates the great variety of commodities made in Scotland and is a fitting expression of the importance of Scotland as a great centre of manufacture. One major disadvantage of Clydeside has been the absence of a large graving dock. Now the new spacious dock at Greenock will provide dry dock facilities, for the first time, for large size vessels, including tankers.

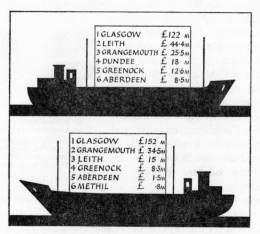

1 GLASGOW	£122 M
2 LEITH	£ 44·4M
3 GRANGEMOUTH	£ 25·5M
4 DUNDEE	£ 18 M
5 GREENOCK	£ 12·6M
6 ABERDEEN	£ 8·5M

1 GLASGOW	£152 M
2 GRANGEMOUTH	£ 34·5M
3 LEITH	£ 15 M
4 GREENOCK	£ 8·3M
5 ABERDEEN	£ 1·5M
6 METHIL	£ ·8M

Fig. 42 Value of Imports (*above*) and Exports (*below*)
at principal Scottish ports

The East of Scotland. Trading activities along the east coast differ in a number of respects from those on the west. There is no counterpart to Glasgow. The east coast ports are not backed by such an immediate and industrial hinterland. Commercial activities are not, therefore, on such a vast scale. In the export traffic, there is a marked reduction.

On the other hand, the river entrances are good natural inlets along which have been constructed docks with ample berths. Many ports lie on either side of the Firth of Forth. They face and are near to centres of supply and demand in the northern part of Europe. It is with this zone that much of their trade is conducted, particularly with Scandinavia and the Low Countries. It is true that their trade extends beyond the North Sea but it is not on such a large scale nor is it so varied in nature as that experienced by the Clyde ports.

In a category by themselves are the three ports of Leith, Grangemouth, and Dundee. Their trade is relatively great in respect of tonnage. They all handle imports in quantity and both Leith and Grangemouth have a large export trade. Leith has long been an established port of east Scotland. Its volume of imports far exceeds its exports. Particularly important are the shipments of grain from North America. Through Leith, also, comes a regular supply of dairy produce and other foodstuffs, some iron and non-ferrous metals, timber and wood products, seeds, fertilisers, and fruits. Outwards, every year, go cargoes of typical Scottish products – beer and whisky, iron and steel goods, paper, coal, and textile manufactures. Granton imports cargoes of esparto grass and some timber.

Grangemouth is an important port but, in contrast to Leith, its development has been most rapid during the present century. It owes much of its expansion to its favourable location. It is situated well up the Forth to accommodate incoming sea traffic and, at the same time, it is within easy distance of the industrial Clydeside. As such, it is involved in handling imports for and exports from the entire Forth-Clyde area. Softwood timber and wood-pulp (Scandinavia), esparto grass (North Africa), petroleum (Caribbean and Middle East), and iron ore (Sweden), are its major imports. In addition a pipe-line from Finnart on Loch Long (where deep water opens into the Firth of Clyde) now conveys crude oil to the town's refineries. From Grangemouth are shipped coal, refined oil, whisky, textiles, iron and steel goods, machinery in many forms and floor coverings. The expansion of industry and the development of the coal resources of the neighbourhood point to further economic progress in Grangemouth and its importance as a port is likely to increase.

In the case of Dundee, a large proportion of its imports is in the form of jute and flax fibres, the former in great quantities from Pakistan and the latter from Belgium. Dundee also receives regular shipments of sawn timber and wood pulp from Scandinavia. Its exports are of a general nature. They reflect the main industries of the town but are not so important as the output of ships, which, though never large in size, make a major contribution, in value, to the export figures of the town.

The ports of Aberdeen, Kirkcaldy, Burntisland, and Inverness make up a group in which imports are far more important than exports. Aberdeen's main imports are paper-making materials like wood-pulp and esparto grass, softwood timber, grain and fertilisers. Without its output of ships, the export trade of the port would be very small in value. Kirkcaldy's imports, far greater than the exports, are mostly concerned with the manufacture of linoleum with which the name of the town is usually associated. The basic material of the industry is cork derived from the cork oak in Mediterranean lands. Great cargoes of granulated cork are imported from Portugal and North Africa. For the same purpose, oilseeds, particularly linseeds, and linseed oil arrive from Canada and Argentina. Although Kirkcaldy's floor coverings are in demand in lands as far apart as Australia and Canada, the consignments are sent mainly to Glasgow for overseas transhipment. Burntisland has valuable imports of bauxite from Ghana in West Africa for its important aluminium industry and its production of ships raises the value of its exports. The port of Inverness has never been able to cope with large imports but it now receives fuel oil for local distribution. Improvements to the quays and channels may increase the port's value as a centre of distribution for northern Scotland.

The port of Methil has a lively import and export trade. It is the main port for handling exports of coal from the Fife coalfield. Coal accounts for its entire export trade. Its imports are mostly connected with the paper industry – wood pulp, esparto and similar grasses and chemicals.

In general, the geographical conditions of the import and export trade of Scotland are:

(1) Concentration of trade at a small number of ports.
(2) Main ports situated on navigable firths in the Central Lowlands, zone of greatest concentration of population.
(3) Glasgow, lying well upstream, the premier port of Scotland.
(4) Main ports backed by hinterland of great industrial potential.
(5) Short haulage distances by road and rail from ports to industrial areas.

Part Two: Regional

XII · THE CENTRAL LOWLANDS – GENERAL

THE Central Lowlands contain the greatest concentration of population in Scotland. In this area is the nucleus of the economic, political, and cultural life of the whole country. For at least two centuries, from the Highlands, the Southern Uplands and, to a lesser but noteworthy extent, from Ireland, people came to settle in and create the towns and cities of central Scotland. It is an area of intense urban development. Indeed, it is this element which gives the central part of Scotland a regional personality. It represents the extent of the social and economic growth of Scotland since the beginning of the eighteenth century. Many and varied are the causes of this development but here they may be simply expressed as a sort of nexus of historical and geographical circumstances.

1. The fortuitous coincidence of coal and iron-ore, especially in quantity in the northern part of Lanarkshire. The former is diminishing in Lanarkshire, the latter is no longer mined but, by dint of such an initial impetus, the metallurgical industry, in all its branches, is still maintained in a very flourishing state.

2. The development of industrial activities of great magnitude and variety, consequent upon a bountiful and convenient supply of coal, the basis of the power-potential in use in factories; the growth of urban centres, a concomitant of factory development.

3. The existence of waterways – natural and man-improved – on both coasts of the area, permitting the maintenance of import and export traffic upon which the majority of the lowland industrial activities depend for permanent survival.

4. The presence of much territory of easy gradient, fostering the establishment of road and rail communications via (a) the level riverlands (b) the gaps through the hill groups, and (c) the man-made bridges over the major river estuaries.

5. The existence of lowlands, of greater extent than in the

8   105

northern Highland zone, whose soil, superior generally, may also be more easily maintained in a higher state of productivity and under more genial climatic conditions. Here exists an agricultural community, e.g. in the Ayrshire plain, in the carselands of Forth and Tay, in Strathmore and in Clydesdale, experiencing the benefits of good communications, and within easy reach, by road and by bus services, of large centres of demand, of market towns and of places of entertainment. The volcanic ranges and the outlying hills of the Southern Uplands reduce the arable area but serve as valuable sheep grazings and their numerous lochs are utilised as reservoirs of drinking water by many of the burghs.

6. It is idle to gainsay these geographical circumstances yet the economic development of the Central Lowlands could not have been possible without the ingenuity, skill and enterprise of individuals, families or industrial concerns, alike in Kilmarnock as in Kirkcaldy, in Motherwell and in Montrose, in Clydebank and in Dundee and in many other towns. Time and again, the geographical circumstances were matched by the will and application of one person or a group of people in the first instance. Such people, accepting the spirit of the Industrial Revolution of the eighteenth and nineteenth centuries, took the initiative in establishing factories and workshops which, by what may be styled as 'industrial inertia', still flourish and play a supreme part in maintaining Scottish production even though the original character of their work may have vanished or suffered a complete change. In examining and determining the geographical factors which prompted the localisation of particular activities in central Scotland, human effort may be as contributory a cause as local geographical conditions, not only in providing the initial impulse to the activity but also in sustaining and directing it in its subsequent stages of development.

7. Finally, for a number of reasons, such as combating unemployment, due to phases of bad trade, or to modernisation of Scotland's traditional industries, there now appear, both in the east and west of the region, a number of Industrial Estates. They exert a profound influence on Scotland's economic activity because their light industries bring a new and additional emphasis to industrial output. The locations of the Estates are planned with care. Their factories are small units and as electricity is their main source of power, they are not so dependent on proximity to coal. Their lay-out is on

modern lines, the conditions of work attractive and they provide employment for large numbers of women workers. But even more important, the factories manufacture or assemble an impressive

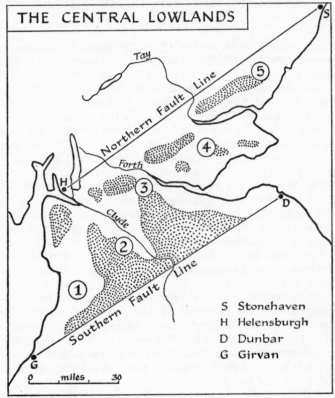

FIG. 43

range of small and light products which, in finding an interested market abroad, furnish more strength and variety to Scotland's export trade.

The Central Lowlands, bounded on the north and south by the familiar line of faults, may be divided into five main regions (shown in the map above) for further study.

XIII · THE CENTRAL LOWLANDS
AYRSHIRE AND THE CLYDE VALLEY

AYRSHIRE

LYING adjacent to the Firth of Clyde, the county of Ayr contains many low sandy coastal tracts and level raised beaches from which gently rolling land rises to an inland crescent of rough moor and clay-covered upland. In the north of the county, the Kilbirnie Hills and the Fenwick Moor of Cunningham are broken by lower corridors leading to the Clyde valley. The Kyle Hills in the east and the Carrick Uplands extending to Loch Ryan in the south are more elevated with summits rising above 2,000 feet on the Ayrshire borders. The rivers, their sources in the bleak inland hills, flow in gently graded courses across the county and drain into the Firth of Clyde. None are very large. In the north, the rivers Garnock and Irvine contribute to a long basin-like estuary before joining the river Clyde. The river Ayr runs across central Ayrshire to the broad Ayr Bay which also receives the Doon Water emerging from Loch Doon on the south-east border.

The climate of Ayrshire is similar to that of western Scotland. The high upland rim experiences lower temperatures. There is much cloud, and copious rain, carried inland by the prevailing westerly winds, renders hill and moorland soft and boggy, particularly in the winter months. But in central Ayrshire and even more so in the western fringe, the decrease in altitude means a reduction in rainfall as well as milder, fog and frost-free winter conditions. The coastal margin around Ayr, sheltered somewhat by the lofty summits of Arran, is both very dry (average annual rainfall 30 inches approximately) and very sunny.

With such a climatic advantage and with level fields, this coastal strip is well suited to the conduct of arable farming. Oats have always been the principal grain crop; barley is now of importance but little wheat is grown. Market gardening is a more recent development in the vicinity of Ayr, tomatoes being the main summer product of the glasshouses with flowers and vegetables during the rest of the year. Ayrshire is second to Lanarkshire in the area devoted to glasshouses. Potato cultivation is the chief agricultural

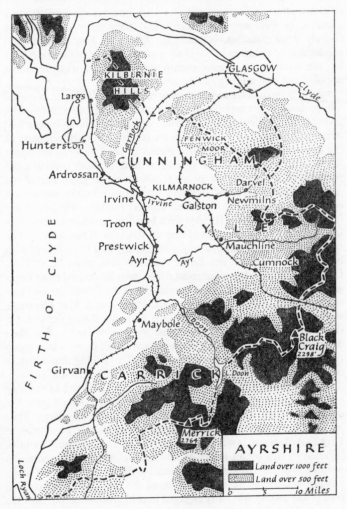

FIG. 44

feature of the Ayrshire coast, especially so in the Girvan and West Kilbride areas. The more genial winters permit farmers to start planting in February and March and their early crop, almost entirely ware potatoes, is ready for lifting in June. The annual production of potatoes in Ayrshire is small relative to that of Angus but the Ayrshire varieties of potato, early on the market, are most popular and find a ready sale in central Scotland.

Likewise, proximity to many great centres of population occasion a huge demand for supplies of fresh milk. The emphasis in Ayrshire farming is on dairying. Dairy farms, seldom very large in size and frequently family units, exist in all the central and northern parts of the county, with easy and quick means of road and rail transport for the disposal of milk. The rearing of herds of dairy cows and the production of milk are the prime factors in the organisation of the farms. Except that grass, hay and turnips in quantity are always essential, there is not a very well defined rotation. Pasture is the farmers' great interest. The Ayrshire breed of cow has a reputation for making the most efficient use of pastures. They have a fine record of milk production as regards quantity and in respect of high butter fat content (4 per cent). Ayrshire milk cows lie in from October to April when their indoor feed must be derived from farm-grown fodder plus cattle cake purchased by the farmer on his visits to the weekly markets at Kilmarnock, Paisley, and Ayr. The cattle stocks are attested and, in the milking parlours, the equipment, for the most part electrical, is up-to-date and maintained in first class condition. In south Ayrshire, there are many hill farms where sheep rearing is important but it is through its dairy farming that Ayrshire has acquired a renown which is unique in Scottish farming.

Yet the economic life of this county is not restricted to farming activities, for its population is mainly urban in type. Apart from Ayr and Kilmarnock, none of the Ayrshire towns are very large. They are small centres of population such as the coastal townships of Largs, Ardrossan, and Troon which, in the summer months, increase in size by an influx of holiday makers. Inland, there is a number of small manufacturing centres in the Irvine valley but many villages and towns have grown around the coal pits. The northern part of the county was early engaged in coal production but now the main coal mining area is in central Ayrshire and on the Dumfries-shire border. The Cumnock district has a large output. With its production of several thousands of tons daily, Killoch colliery is one of the most up-to-date and productive in Scotland. The Ayrshire coalfield produces 3·7 million tons annually. Ayrshire coals are good in quality, useful for household, gas, electricity and industrial purposes and are distributed over a wide area of south-west Scotland while some is shipped through Ayr to Ireland.

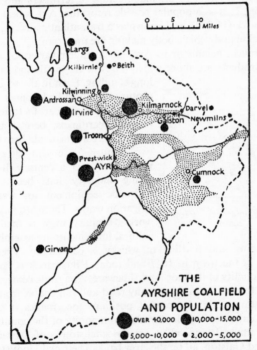

FIG. 45

The customary association of coal with steam and electric power is reflected in the variety of Ayrshire industries. The largest towns are Ayr (45,000) and Kilmarnock (48,000). As an early settlement, **Ayr** was first a ford and later a bridge point over its river; it was a garrison town and once the chief port of the west of Scotland. Its present importance may well date from the middle of last century when Ayr was linked by rail with Glasgow. As a market centre, Ayr has always been noteworthy but rail services and, later, bus facilities rendered it exceedingly attractive as a popular summer resort. It is not an important port, the coal trade with Ireland being its main activity. Its industries are small in size and varied in character. There are forges, ship repairing works, knitwear, footwear and carpet factories in addition to the manufacture of fertilisers and farming appliances. It is as a popular seaside resort that Ayr is best known. At Prestwick (11,000), well known as a transatlantic airport, aircraft construction and vehicle body making are important.

Kilmarnock, neighbour to Ayr, has a similar variety of industry but its products are more widely known. Its textile industry is of

Fig. 46 Kilmarnock – a route centre

long standing. Even in the seventeenth century, the town had bonnet makers. Its modern knitwear factories make jumpers, cardigans, berets, and balmorals. Its carpets, made here for over two centuries, are sent all over the world. For over a century, its engineering industry has been making hydraulic equipment for water and irrigation works. There are locomotive works; sanitary ware is made; agricultural implements are assembled and the blending and bottling of whisky is carried on. There were skinners in the town in 1647 and today Kilmarnock is famed for the high quality of its boot- and shoeware. As a route centre, it has a fine site for on it converge many road and rail routes from across the Ayrshire plain. Its central position, too, makes it a fitting market centre serving the farming community of the county.

In the upper Irvine valley, are the small towns of Darvel, Newmilns, and Galston, all on the river bank. Their main industry is the manufacture of lace, curtains, netting, brise-bise, etc. As the old handloom domestic weaving pursuit died out, the textile workers, accustomed to the technique of making Madras cloth and gauze, developed their own power lace looms and succeeded in evolving a lace industry which has a turnover per worker greater than that of Nottingham. The small factory units of these little towns constitute a main centre for the production of lace and curtain netting in

Great Britain, and enormous quantities are exported to all parts of the world.

At Ardrossan (9,000), a cross channel port, an oil refinery produces bitumen. There is a little ship building and repair work while near the town is Ardeer chemical centre. Glengarnock steelworks turns out rails and ships' parts. Hunterston Nuclear Station, opposite the Cumbraes, is now producing electricity for the national grid.

THE CLYDE VALLEY

The river Clyde rises on the Dumfriesshire-Lanarkshire border in the Southern Uplands. It flows in a northerly direction round Tinto (2,335 feet) and descends abruptly in the region of Lanark. The river then traverses a low plain (nowhere over 250 feet) until, below Glasgow, it becomes a navigable channel and passes westwards to the Tail o' the Bank. There, in a southerly bend, the waterway widens out past Bute, the Cumbraes, and Arran into a broad firth, with Ailsa Craig (Paddy's milestone) prominent as a precipitous stump in midstream between Kintyre and the Ayrshire coast. The river Clyde thus travels through most of the western lowlands of Scotland. It is the main drainage channel of Lanarkshire and it also receives the rivers of the adjacent counties.

Its upper course lies high up in the Lowther Hills, an important watershed of southern Scotland. There, at over 2,000 feet, many hill streams, one being the Clydes Burn, tumble into the Potrail, Daer and Elvan Waters and their combined volume make up the youthful river Clyde. Thus far, the upper Clyde cuts through remote and sterile hills and moorland, but at Roberton the river clears the southern boundary faultline. Its valley is more open and level fields border the river. In direction, its course is most erratic. Around Tinto the river wanders in a detour until, above Lanark, it receives the Douglas Water on its left bank.

The middle course of the river extends from Lanark to Motherwell. At first, for a few miles above and below Lanark (overlooking the Clyde), the river is suddenly constricted to a narrow and precipitous gorge of natural rock masonry. Over horizontal shelvings of red sandstone, the river cascades in a series of waterfalls at Bonnington Linn, again at Corra Linn and, once more, at Stonebyres Linn. When the river emerges from this spectacular defile, it

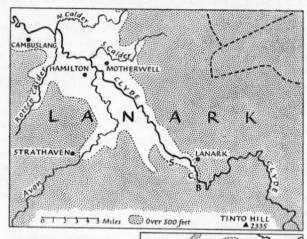

B Bonnington Linn
C Corra Linn
S Stonebyres Linn

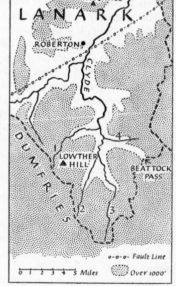

FIG. 47 Map of the head waters of the river Clyde (*right*) and middle Clyde valley (*above*)

1 Elvan Water
2 Potrail Water
3 Daer Water
4 Clydes Burn

flows more serenely and along its banks are broad and level holms set in orchard or tree clad slopes. Several miles downstream, the main river is joined by the river Avon, the point of confluence being visible from the Motherwell-Hamilton road.

Below Motherwell, the Clyde enters its lower course. The lands on either side of the river continue flat and low. The river itself runs through the great industrial area of Clydeside, its waters being utilised by many factories lining the river banks. The river is tidal up to the weir at Carmyle just above Glasgow but the navigable waterway runs from the Broomielaw Quay at Glasgow to the Tail o' the Bank at Greenock. By way of the pretty Kelvingrove, the Kelvin, its lower waters polluted by industrial effluents, joins the Clyde at Partick, Glasgow. Lower down, opposite Clydebank, the river Cart enters the main river. The White Cart, passing through Paisley, is soon joined by the Black Cart. Into it drains the Gryfe Water which, in its descent from the Renfrew Heights, flows in a direction exactly opposite to that of the river Clyde. From Loch Lomond the river Leven drops gently through its vale to enter the main waterway by Dumbarton Rock. The lower channel of the river Clyde is much beset by mud banks but deep water is reached at the Tail o' the Bank (i.e. at the end of the sand banks). Then, as this great waterway makes an abrupt turn into the Firth, the sea-arms of Loch Long, the Holy Loch, and the Gare Loch reach back to an imposing screen of rugged mountain tops which make up the landward horizon to the north.

The river Clyde is not a long river (about 100 miles) but its lower course is unrivalled as a navigable waterway. There is no similar channel which extends so far inland along the entire coast of western Scotland. Its westerly location has made it the premier trade route of Scotland and within the cluster of towns which exist around its lower course live over one-third of the entire population of Scotland.

Agriculture in the Clyde Valley

The rolling grassy hills of the Southern Uplands, drained by the headstreams of the river Clyde, provide a distinct contrast to the great ruggedness of the northern Highlands. The main occupation is that of hill-farming. Over this great expanse of hill and moor, the rough pasture and heather, ample though it is, is ill suited for any other activity but sheep grazing. There are great flocks of robust Blackface sheep as well as some Cheviot and Crossbreed types. During the inclement winter months, many sheep farmers take their animals, the Cheviots and the best lambs, from the higher grazings and bring them down to the more sheltered areas in the main and tributary valleys. There, at lower levels, dairy farms exist for the grass is richer and herds of Ayrshire dairy cows are pastured. On such farms as in the Biggar district there are always fields of potatoes but oats, hay and turnips are also grown as food for the dairy herds which are kept indoors in the winter. The dairy farms are not so remote as the hill farms but the whole of this upper part of the valley is very rural. Few people live here and places like Biggar (1,500) are small market centres.

In the middle course, from the market town of Lanark (6,000) through several small towns and villages to the vicinity of Mother-well, the outstanding occupation is that of fruit farming and market gardening. The haughs or valley bottoms for a few miles on both sides of the main river and its tributaries are level enough to be well worked. There are beds of soft fruit like strawberries as well as a great number of nurseries in which glasshouses contain the majority of the Scottish tomato crop which comes on the market in the summer months. On the slopes above the rivers there are more nurseries. Soft fruits are again popular and there are fields of goose-berry and currant bushes and row after row of apple and plum trees. In the late spring, the bushes and orchards are clad in a mantle of white and pink blossom, a promise, if frost does not interfere, of a bountiful harvest in the summer and autumn. The fruit is sent to the Glasgow area and some is used in local jam factories, e.g. at Carluke. During the winter months, the nurserymen produce vegetables and fresh flowers out of season.

In this, the most fertile part of the Clyde valley, there have been orchards for many a century. Of the soft fruits, the strawberry acquired spectacular popularity at the close of last century. When disease at length ravaged the crop, fruit growers were perforce attracted to glasshouse produce. Now, although fruit types resistant to many diseases are in use, market gardening has not diminished in importance. Indeed, Lanarkshire is the county with the largest area of glasshouses.

In the lower Clyde area, mining and industrial activities together with the expansion of towns greatly reduce the area available for the practice of agriculture. Mixed farming is the common pursuit. At no great distance from urban centres, there are fields of oats, potatoes and turnips as well as grazings for cattle. The enormous and constant demand for fresh milk in the Clydeside towns makes dairying supremely important. On most farms, hay and grass are essential, so much so that hard and fast rotations do not exist and crops for sale are relatively unimportant.

On the northern and eastern outskirts of Glasgow, pig fattening is carried on. Pigs thrive on a variety of food, but swill, hygienically prepared and mixed with ground oats and raw potatoes, forms the greater part of pig-feed. From the local urban districts the supply of swill is ample and regular.

At a few miles from Glasgow, there are many market garden holdings. Nurserymen grow a wide range of fresh domestic vegetables as well as glasshouse produce. The number of glasshouses is very great, e.g. in the neighbourhood of Torrance on the river Kelvin. Another activity of a special nature is the commercial production of rhubarb. Not very far out of Glasgow, entire fields are devoted to this product, which finds its way to various jam factories in Central Scotland and England.

The Industrial Geography of the Clyde Valley

The industrial geography of the Clyde valley is concerned with the lower part of the river basin. This industrial belt, the most concentrated and productive in all Scotland, extends from Motherwell in central Lanarkshire through the city of Glasgow, through the manufacturing towns of Renfrewshire and Dunbartonshire as far as Greenock at the Tail o' the Bank. Many of the towns form a tight cluster, one built-up area passing almost unnoticeably into the next. Dominating the entire region is the city of Glasgow. Into and out of it, every day, travel many thousands of workers from every direction. The towns around Glasgow are near enough to make it easy to suggest that they are offsprings of the parent city. But this is not exactly the case for, although their activities are often similar, each town has its particular industrial outlook and responsibility and they all insist on their own identity. Three separate zones can, therefore, be recognised: (1) The Lanarkshire industrial area. (2) The city of Glasgow. (3) The lower Clyde towns.

1. The Lanarkshire Industrial Towns

It was in Lanarkshire that the iron industry of Scotland made its greatest expansion. As early as 1780, ironstone was worked in Carnwath near Carstairs. Of greater importance, however, was the discovery of blackband ironstone in the Monkland district. It was particularly abundant and valuable, too, because it occurred along with large quantities of coal. In the Govan district, also, there existed other ironstones yielding about 30 per cent of iron. But the blackband ironstone was the main source of raw material in the iron industry of the first half of the nineteenth century.

Central Lanarkshire had coal in plenty, especially the hard splint coal which was the best for smelting iron. The early blast furnaces were vastly improved by the introduction of the hot blast. At once the cost of iron production was greatly reduced and there followed a great expansion of the iron industry. As a consequence, remarkable economic and social changes took place in the county as indeed in most of the lower Clyde valley. Places which had been mere hamlets or villages at the start of the nineteenth century flourished, by mid-century, into industrial townships, rapidly filling up with people. To each came settlers from every part of Scotland as well as from Ireland. Houses sprang up as quickly as factories and there was much work for the inhabitants.

Coal and iron were in constant demand as both were vital to the industrial development of the entire valley. The supply of iron in the Monkland area gave Airdrie and Coatbridge a great start in the iron industry. The population of Airdrie jumped from 6,500 (1831) to 14,000 (1851) and Coatbridge with less than 1,000 inhabitants rose to over 8,000 by 1851. Later on, after 1870, when the use and manufacture of steel became common, Motherwell and its neighbourhood sprang into industrial importance. By this time, however, local supplies of iron-ore were near exhaustion. The steel industry now draws on imports of ore from such sources as Canada, Sweden, North and West Africa. The iron and steel industry of Lanarkshire is thus able to carry on even after the original sources of iron ore have been used up.

The Lanarkshire coal resources have not yet been completely used up although there have been recent mine closures. The present rate of extraction in the Central Coalfield, extending over much of the county, is just over 3 million tons. Although many seams are relatively thin, there is still coal to be had from the pits in the vicinity of Coatbridge and in the eastern section of the area. From the Lanarkshire pits come household and industrial coals; among the latter, coking coals are now of special importance to the Scottish iron and steel industry. Today there are many new and varied industrial pursuits within its borders but Lanarkshire's traditional industries are connected with coal, iron and steel.

Two simple but noteworthy factors help to account for the intense industrialisation of Lanarkshire: (i) the unique, initial store of coal and iron; (ii) the ingenuity, perseverance and technical experience of local workers and businessmen. This latter influence is apparent in the modern industrial developments which have taken place in the county over the last decade.

Motherwell and Wishaw (73,000). A century ago, Motherwell was but a village of 1,300 inhabitants. It derived some importance as a junction for railways which were then being developed for the transport of coal and iron. Industry came as late as 1871 when an iron-works was set up near some local coal. Soon after, the new industry of steel making was started at Colville's Dalziel Works. As more steel works opened up, Motherwell soon became a great centre for steel manufacture. Imported ore travels 15 miles by rail from Glasgow docks to the steel works which produce steel plates, girders, beams, etc. for ship building as well as for constructional work like bridge and crane building. At Ravenscraig (and its sister plant nine miles away at Gartcosh), there is Scotland's first and only steel strip mill. This vast new plant, wholly integrated, supplies coils and coils of thin sheet steel and light plate, so essential to the new vehicle works and to factories that make consumer goods like refrigerators and washing machines. The new plant is designed to foster industrial growth of this sort in the Central Lowlands and, thus, to create diversity in Scotland's industrial economy. Wishaw, part of Motherwell since 1920, has steel works and also produces clothing and confectionery. It is a market town for the rural neighbourhood. Smaller towns like Bellshill and Mossend are associated with steel activities.

Hamilton (42,000), situated above the marshy confluence of rivers Clyde and Avon, is a town of great antiquity. Although there are steel works not far away and an industrial estate at Blantyre,

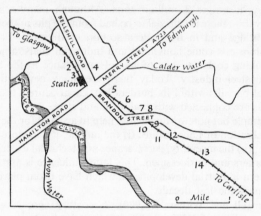

FIG. 48 The location of the main industries of
Motherwell

1. Electrical engineering works
2. Sugar machinery factory
3. Bridge and structural engineering works
4. Structural engineering works
5. Dalziel Steel Works
6. Railway rolling stock works (now taken
   over by 5)
7. Steel works

8. Mining equipment factory
9. Iron and steel works
10. Steel works
11. Structural engineering works
12. Iron and steel works
13. Light steel works
14. Wagons, tanks, mining plant

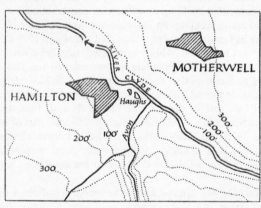

FIG. 49 The sites of Hamilton and Motherwell

Hamilton is not and never has been a great centre of industry. There are printing, textile, nuts and bolts, electric lamp and valve factories. Its new multi-storey County Buildings point to its importance as a regional administrative centre. It is a shopping and market centre, with several race meetings during the year.

East Kilbride (39,000*), a spacious new town created to take part of Glasgow's overspill population, is designed on modern lines, with housing and residential parts, a town shopping centre and industrial areas. Its industrial development is far from complete but the number of factories already operating is great and their output embraces an astonishing range of products, e.g. aero engines, soft drinks, foodstuffs, cosmetics, instruments, tools, carpets and ladies clothing. By such a diversity of industrial structure, the town has made a rapid advancement and its ultimate population is expected to be 70,000.

Rutherglen (25,000) is south of the river Clyde and on the very outskirts of Glasgow. The oldest of Scottish burghs, dating from the twelfth century, it still remains independent of Glasgow. Coal mines exist in its neighbourhood and it is a town of great industrial activity. Its steel works are most important but there are also chemical works and paper mills, while electric motors, furniture, and foodstuffs are also produced.

Ten miles east of Glasgow is **Coatbridge (54,000)** which traces its industrial importance to the discovery of vast amounts of coal and iron in the district. At one time, however, every local stream was said to have its lint mill because farmers were wont to grow flax. Linen was made at Coatbridge until the introduction of cotton cloth rendered flax growing unprofitable. But early last century, the exploitation of the rich local blackband ores caused iron works to spring to life in the town. Its population, 750 in 1831, rose to 1,500 in 1841 and soared to 8,500 by mid-century. More and more iron works, tube factories and foundries appeared amid the network of new railways. Its iron industry prepared the way for the establishment of the steel works later on. Today, the iron and steel industry remains the mainstay of Coatbridge. Steel strips, plates, washers, nuts, bolts and wire are turned out for engineering purposes. Steel tubes are made, so are huge steel rollers and other plant and

* Estimated 1964.

equipment for iron and steel works. Other industries have developed in the town, notably the manufacture of boilers and the production of firebricks. Coatbridge is one of the major steel centres of Lanarkshire.

Airdrie (34,000) is a close neighbour of Coatbridge. Its foundries and engineering shops manufacture a great range of products like steel tubes, derricks, rivets, bolts, shovels, coils and springs. The town possesses boiler works and foundries which make castings of various types. Other works turn out confectionery and foodstuffs, fibre-glass boats, grit, bricks and clothing. The industrial development of Airdrie has been similar to that of its neighbour. An early textile pursuit in which Airdrie's workers won fame for their skill in weaving gave place to the iron industry when the wealth of local minerals began to be exploited at the start of last century.

2. Glasgow (1,055,000).

Glasgow is the third largest city of Great Britain. Everywhere, its full vigour and industrial energy is at once manifest, in its shipyards and workshops, spacious and old, in its factory estates, well laid out and modern, in its streets of huge tenements and in its great dormitory suburbs. The city extends along both banks of the river Clyde. With each phase of its development, it has stretched, almost like an unburstable balloon, until its outskirts now lie several miles from the city centre. The land on which a large part of the city is built consists of a long and level riverine tract, backed on both the north and south sides of the river by ridges and steep hills or drumlins of glacial origin.

Extreme in diversity is the economic pattern of Glasgow; extraordinary, too, is the sheer size of the city. Well nigh every aspect of its life is influenced by this element of size – it may even be a most grievous weakness in its character. It is, by far, the largest and most populous city in the whole of Scotland but its very magnitude permits no more than reference to a selection of points of geographical importance.

The early growth of Glasgow. The time and place of the earliest settlement is not known for certain nor is there an undisputed explanation of the origin of the place name of 'Glasgow'. A very early settlement is thought to have existed near the present Stockwell Street. Here the river Clyde, broader and shallower than it is now, was joined by the Molendinar Burn. Drinking water was available as well as fish and the river provided an easy fording point. The Romans who occupied the district around Glasgow may also have used this convenient crossing en route for their fortified Antonine wall which extended east-west across central Scotland, passing through the present suburb of Bearsden to the Clyde at Bowling.

About a century and a half after their departure, St. Kentigern (better known as St. Mungo) founded a chapel on the banks of the Molendinar. Thanks to his missionary efforts, an ecclesiastical settlement took shape around this church and this was the rôle in which the hamlet of Glasgow first become known. Several centuries of heathenism followed before Glasgow's ecclesiastical influence was re-asserted, and the first cathedral, built over St. Mungo's grave, was completed in 1136. Before the end of the same century, Glasgow had been granted the status of a burgh with permission to hold an annual fair lasting a week.

The town increased its importance when, about 1350, the first stone bridge was built by Bishop Rae over the river Clyde. It supplanted an older wooden bridge erected at the Stockwell ford over the river. This more substantial bridge, with eight arches affirmed Glasgow as a bridgehead settlement.

The close association of Glasgow with the church led to the grant of a papal bull for the foundation of a university in 1450. Then the population did not exceed 3,000 but already there were merchants in Glasgow, exchanging their cured herring and salmon for French brandy and salt. The number of merchantmen increased as did their business with the Continent but Glasgow, on the west side of Scotland, was too far removed from European markets for trade to be on an extensive scale. Yet, by the close of the seventeenth century, the spirit of commercial endeavour pervaded the town. During the brief period of the Commonwealth, the Glasgow merchants had enjoyed freedom of trade with the colonies in America. Such free exchange did not last long, however, for, at the Restoration, the English Navigation Acts were once more imposed and Scotland was denied trade with America. But the Glasgow merchants soon found ways of evading the restrictions and succeeded in doing business with the American colonies.

By far the greatest stimulus to commercial enterprise in Glasgow was the Act of Union of 1707. This measure provided the impetus which was to generate the full force of transatlantic trade. By it, restrictions on trade in the New World were removed. The entire American market lay within the grasp of the Glasgow merchants. The convenient location of their town gave them an advantage over all east coast ports of Scotland. At once their trading schemes were put into operation.

Thus, by 1707, Glasgow, with about 13,000 inhabitants, was a town of importance with great possibilities. It was a cathedral town, a centre of learning,* a crossing place and a market centre. Above all, it was a town favourably placed for commercial expansion. All of these 'let Glasgow flourish' and they still form a part of the pattern of modern Glasgow.

A Port. 'Probably for no river in Britain has so much been done by art and man's device as for the Clyde above Port Glasgow. In fact, from a mile below Bowling upwards to Glasgow, a length of 12 miles, the Clyde of the present day is as nearly as much an artificial navigation as the Suez Canal. It requires constant dredging to maintain its depth. . . .' James Deas (1876).

This succinct reference to the river Clyde accounts for the paramount contribution which the river has made to the commercial and industrial advancement of Glasgow. The signal achievement of controlling and re-shaping the course and condition of the river was the result of immense efforts of toil, skill and perseverance. A navigable waterway has been created where virtually nothing of the sort existed previously.

For a long time, the river Clyde had little influence on the growth of Glasgow and on the activities of its people. The channel below the town was much obstructed by shallows and fords. Its course was tortuous and the river was badly suited to the passage of even the smallest vessels. The chief encumbrances, well illustrated in Blaeu's Atlas published in Amsterdam (1662), took the form of inches or islands of river-borne silt. Lying in mid-stream, they stretched from the confluence of the river Kelvin to Kilpatrick. Further downstream, about Dumbuck, the river was easily fordable and so shallow as to make uninterrupted navigation impossible except for flat-bottomed boats of very shallow draught.

*The new University of Strathclyde is a recent reinforcement of Glasgow's educational function – particularly for higher technological education.

Such natural handicaps forced the Glasgow merchants to make use of the harbour of Irvine during the seventeenth century and their goods were brought to and from Glasgow by barge or by road. As this was a costly practice, the Glasgow magistrates endeavoured to purchase ground at Dumbarton for the construction of a more

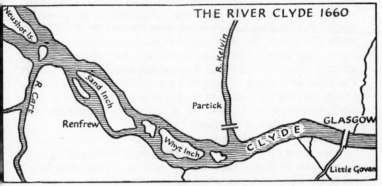

FIG. 50

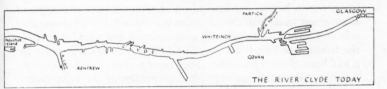

FIG. 51

suitable port. Negotiations fell through and the magistrates thereupon resolved to build a port of their own on the south bank of the upper firth. This was named Port Glasgow and in 1710 it was the principal customs-house port of the river. The channel between Port Glasgow and the small Broomlielaw quay was still, however, only navigable for the merest barge.

The development of trade, as a consequence of the Act of Union, made it imperative that if Glasgow were to flourish, the river must be made completely navigable up to the town centre. Already, by 1772, a great variety of products was exchanged and a brisk trade existed with many European lands as well as with North America and the West Indies. Particularly promising and profitable were the imports from the New World of tobacco, timber and sugar. Indeed Glasgow was now receiving more than half of all the tobacco imported into Britain and its merchants held a very large share of the transhipment trade in tobacco to Europe. It was at this stage that, on the invitation of the magistrates, John Golborne of Chester set about his project for improving navigation on the river. His scheme was designed to narrow the river channel for several miles below Glasgow by the construction of dykes and jetties at various points. They confined the water so that the river exerted a greater scouring effect on its bed and thus cut for itself a deeper channel. The dykes also served to straighten the course of the river and the islands were incorporated into the banks of the river. One of these dykes, known as the 'Lang Dyke', is still visible in the Dumbuck-Dumbarton section of the river.*

Although Golborne's undertaking was the most striking project for controlling the river, there took place many additional improvements which by skilful deepening and prolonged dredging at length converted the river Clyde into a navigable waterway. The systematic improvement of the river combined with the evolution of the steamship to bestow supreme advantages on the port of Glasgow. Its overseas trade with the Americas was extended and commercial relations were established with every part of the world. By 1850, the tonnage of vessels arriving at Glasgow was twice as great as it had been 20 years previously. Such rapid and progressive development demonstrated not only the inadequacy of the river quays but also the urgent need for the construction of docks to accommodate the size and number of vessels using the port.

Kingston Dock was opened in 1867 and, now, with $12\frac{1}{2}$ miles of quays and six tidal dock systems, Glasgow is a very great port, the only noteworthy port on the west of Scotland. Its export and import trade far exceeds, in character and magnitude, that of any other port of Scotland. Some of its docks are especially equipped for dealing with mineral traffic like iron-ore and some for the discharge of grain and timber cargoes. At others, merchant ships, regular visitors to the port, load 'general cargo' – an apt phrase

*Later, on the advice of John Rennie, walls were built to join up the ends of Golborne's jetties and much land along the river front was reclaimed.

for Glasgow is the premier outlet for the entire range of articles made in Scotland.

The peaceful gently sloping riverlands of long ago have thus been transformed into a busy waterfront lined by massive cranes, spacious transit sheds, lofty grain storages, acres of timber yards and animal lairages.

A centre of communications. Though there is a great difference between its modern bridges and that built by Bishop Rae in 1350, the function of the Clyde bridges is very similar. As of old, this is the lowest point in its course that the river has been bridged. Today, Glasgow is of such a size that it extends far over both banks of the river Clyde – one residential district alone has a population larger than Perth. Bridges are as essential for the conduct of its activities as are the people themselves. Within a distance of a mile, from the Broomielaw to Glasgow Green, there are seven bridges. They carry road and rail traffic in and out of the city but even with an underground railway passenger service and a number of vehicular and passenger ferries, the congestion of road traffic is such that additional crossings are necessary. No other city of Scotland has or needs as many river crossings as Glasgow.

The road and railway systems which serve the commercial and social requirements of the city are inevitably intricate. Many bus terminals and two main railway stations, all on the north side, cater for passenger traffic while there are numerous factory sidings and goods depots spread over the city. Some provide storage accommodation and, at others, special wagons are used for dealing with livestock or for transporting rails, girders and great pieces of machinery.

Glasgow is also a major road traffic depot. It is the collecting and distributing centre for all types of merchandise transported by road to and from England. Every day and night, fleets of long distance lorries make Glasgow their starting or finishing point. No other city in Scotland handles such an amount of freight or passenger traffic.

In other ways communications play an important rôle in the city. The provision of fresh food for such a large populace is an enormous task. The city has spacious markets which handle livestock, meat, fish, cheese, fruit, and vegetables. Such perishable foods are brought to the city for retail and distribution by a regular day-to-day service of lorries and goods trains. Livestock reach the cattle-market by a private road from the railway sidings and do not appear in the public streets. On many occasions, road and rail facilities are taxed to the utmost in transporting crowds to sporting events, shows and exhibitions. Glasgow is a most popular centre of recreation and entertainment but it is also fortunate in the attractive countryside by which it is surrounded to the north and to the west. Within easy reach of the city, by road, rail or river steamer, are examples of the finest coast, loch and mountain scenery in Scotland.

Fig. 52

At Whiteinch, towards the west of Glasgow, a twin tunnel is a new and free route under the river Clyde. It provides a most convenient crossing for great numbers of pedestrians and all sorts of vehicles. The tunnel increases Glasgow's importance as a crossing point of the Clyde with routes radiating to the entire Clyde Valley, the Central Lowlands and the rest of Scotland.

A centre of industry. Glasgow, itself, is an enormous industrial centre; it is the most important workshop of Scotland. Yet, before 1700, when the population did not exceed a few thousand inhabitants, its industrial life was without much significance. Industry now provides employment for a large proportion of the male and female working population. Of all the causes which account for this remarkable development, the most outstanding is the Act of Union (1707). This legislative measure provided a unique incentive for Glasgow's commerce. In turn, commerce prompted the upsurge of industrial activity in the town. The freedom of trade permitted by the Union created a market in North America and in the West Indies for manufactured goods, urgently needed by emigrants settling in the undeveloped continent and islands. Thus, in exchange for the tobacco which Glasgow merchants eagerly sought from places like Virginia and Maryland, all sorts of articles of necessity were required as return cargoes to the New World. Never had arisen an opportunity more favourable to manufacture in Glasgow. This transatlantic commerce fostered the spirit of manufacture in the town, on a scale and with an energy which had never previously existed.

Linen manufacture, begun by 1725, was one of Glasgow's important industries. Legislative measures, which prohibited the import of French cambrics and provided a bounty on all linen exported, contributed to the prosperity of this textile pursuit. Glasgow-made linen, ranging from inkle (tape) to printed cloths, was a major export to the Americas. Noteworthy also was the tanning of leather and both manufactured footwear and saddlery were despatched overseas. So was glass, made in Glasgow from 1730. Ale was also exported as well as all sorts of ironmongery made in the town.

A rich trade in tobacco existed: both manufactured snuff and tobacco went back to the land of their origin. But the opulent tobacco traffic came to an end when the American War of Independence (1775-83) put a sudden stoppage to supplies for a time. Glasgow's commercial interests thereupon switched to the Caribbean area of Central America. Sugar and cotton became the leading imports from the West Indies. The first led to sugar refining and, very soon, cotton ousted linen as the principal textile fibre used in Glasgow. The manufacturers were not slow to adopt the new mechanical devices which effected great advances in the production of cotton yarn. Then, as soon as steam power became possible in factories, the cotton industry experienced its greatest expansion since it profited from three geographical advantages: (1) the port and navigable river Clyde, serving as the essential instrument of trade; (2) the abundant supply of coal, for raising steam power in the factories; (3) the humid atmosphere of the west, providing a safeguard against the snapping of the cotton fibres in the machines.

Thus favoured, the cotton industry enjoyed a very rapid rise to prosperity during the first half of the last century. It suffered a heavy blow, however, when, at the time of the American Civil War (1861) supplies of raw cotton from the Southern States were cut off. When cotton fibre was again available, the Glasgow cotton manufacturers had perforce to follow a more specialised branch of their trade because of the development of large scale cotton production in Lancashire. Thus it is that, nowadays, fine quality cotton is made up into the superior shirting for which Glasgow's east-end factories justly derive a world wide reputation. Gingham, poplins, laces, along with light, striped and checked cotton pieces and muslins, are all produced in the city, much of this textile output being destined for a thriving export trade.

Glasgow's textile efforts are not limited to cotton piece goods. There are many factories, large and small, which make use of both natural and modern man-made fibres in the production of a wide variety of textile goods and covering fabrics. With a century of experience and sustained by supplies of woollen yarns, carpet making is one of the most important branches of the textile industry. Glasgow-made carpets are produced in great quantities and find a ready market all over the world. Other branches of the industry such as weaving, spinning, dyeing, finishing, and bleaching flourish and all provide employment for a great number of women workers. Glasgow is a most important textile centre.

Simultaneously with the rise of the cotton trade came the development of Glasgow's iron industry. Whereas the former was served by supplies of raw cotton from abroad, the latter profited from a number of purely local circumstances. All around Glasgow there existed an abundant supply of coal, essential for iron smelting. Ironstone was plentiful too and the mining of both minerals was soon on a large scale. Of supreme importance, also, was the remarkable phase of industrial discovery and innovation centred in and around Glasgow in the first part of last century. David Mushet, of the Clyde Ironworks, found that the blackband ores near Glasgow – in the Coatbridge-Airdrie district – could be smelted (1801). Henry Bell propelled the Comet, driven by a 4 h.p. engine, down the river Clyde (1812). This early use of steam power for navigation was made possible by Watt's previous perfection of the steam engine as much as by the control and deepening of the river Clyde. Then, in 1828, James Neilson, of the Glasgow Gas Co., applied the device of the hot blast furnace, a smelting process more economic and thrice as efficient. Later still, Robert Napier, already well known in Glasgow as a marine engineer, collaborated in 1840 with Samuel Cunard in the construction of steam-driven iron vessels capable of maintaining a regular North Atlantic passenger service.

Meanwhile, the introduction of railways during this same period provided another form of steam transport. The early railways, such as the Monkland-Kirkintilloch line, were of a local character. As the iron and ship building industries expanded, however, they became first and foremost the essential means of transport of raw materials and finished goods. Out of the extraordinary mid-century boom in railway line construction in Scotland grew the great locomotive industry of Glasgow.

The chief industries of Glasgow thus emerged with the Industrial Revolution. Coal and iron, engineering and ship-building, locomotive and railway construction, all contributed to the metallurgical industry of the city. From its iron and steel activities (steel making dating from the late 1870's) the city of Glasgow derived its present industrial importance. The hinterland was bereft of mineral richness yet the heavy industries were still maintained. The modern requirements of raw materials like iron ore and high grade coke were brought into the area from as far apart as Newfoundland and north-east England. But, above all, heavy industry in Glasgow was endowed with the accumulated experience and technical skill of its engineers and craftsmen, and this persists as the major factor today.

Glasgow is known the world over for its ship-building. Its shipyards, lining both banks of the river, turn out all sorts of vessels – large size tankers, cargo and passenger ships, coasters and ferries, tugs and harbour craft as well as warships. Along the river front, powerful cranes rise high above a network of stanchions and scaffoldings which embrace the vessels-to-be. The river is narrow but as the slipways run aslant to the channel, the largest of vessels can be launched and manoeuvred into the fitting out basin. The launch of a new vessel marks the completion of one major operation but in the fitting out basin, the engines and boilers are installed, navigational gear supplied, refrigeration and electrical plant with miles of cabling fitted, air-conditioning and ventilation apparatus fixed and a vast stock of furnishings and equipment put aboard. Only when the entire construction of a ship is completed, from the laying of the keel to the trials in the Firth and the maiden voyage, is it possible to appreciate how many other Glasgow industries and workers are involved and are dependent on this vital industry.

In huge workshops and forges, Glasgow engineers design and produce an amazing variety of heavy steel manufactures like wheels and axles, steel crankshafts and gear wheels, boiler drums and propellers, mining equipment, rolling plant for steel mills and armour plating. Another branch of this industry is that of constructional engineering in which Glasgow has a reputation for the production of steel erections and installations. Fixed and open bridges, dock gates, caissons, cranes, tanks, pipelines and power station plant are regular undertakings of Glasgow firms for home and overseas customers. The construction of locomotives, so long a traditional pursuit of Glasgow, has ceased, although repairs and maintenance of equipment remains. One branch of the transport industry that flourishes is the production of motor vehicles and coach building – lorries, buses, etc. Associated with this type of work is the manufacture, on a large scale, of vehicular rubber tyres and tubes.

There is much more to the industrial strength of Glasgow than ships, textiles and engineering products. Thousands of people, from Glasgow and its vicinity, find employment in activities that seldom receive very special mention. In small factories and obscure workshops, skilled men and women turn out an entire range of children's garments and adults' clothing. The costumes, suitings, duffle coats, etc., which they design, are made up in anticipation of each season's demands. An offshoot of this clothing industry is the manufacture of raincoats and umbrellas. Situated near the docks are mills that require imported oilseeds to make animal feeding stuffs. Glasgow's chemical industry includes the production of phosphates, detergents, disinfectants and soaps; in this category, too, is the manufacture of matches. Food and drinks are made in different parts of the city. Bread-making is always important. There are flour, grain and sugar mills and factories that make the technical machinery and equipment for such mills. Fruit juices, aerated waters, coffee, sauces, beer and whisky form an important beverage group, with whisky the most valuable of all as an export. Great quantities of industrial and domestic paints, enamels and varnishes are made. The paper and publishing industry is strongly represented. Regular shipments of Canadian newsprint are required for the daily and weekly newspapers printed in Glasgow; its publishers produce novels, bibles and textbooks.

Cartons, tissues, cardboard and corrugated packing are special paper products. There is no end to the variety of products made in the city.

The development of light industry, as distinct from traditional pursuits already mentioned, is a noteworthy feature of the industrial enterprise of Glasgow, as indeed of the entire Lower Clyde area. Light industries came to the west of Scotland in the 1930's when world trade recessions affected the capital industries of Clydeside

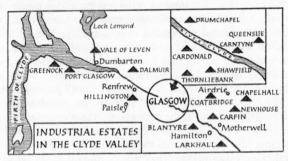

FIG. 53

and brought much hardship and great unemployment in their wake. The situation was made worse by the diminution in the local coal resources. By the introduction of light industries, the whole industrial structure of Clydeside was put on a broader and more varied basis. New industries, in keeping with the technical advances of the century, were encouraged and they provide work in plenty, particularly for male technicians as well as for thousands of women operatives.

The industrial estates are modern in appearance and they are smoke-free since they rely on electricity as their source of power. The small-size rented factories provide good conditions of work with up-to-date amenities. Glasgow, itself, has five such estates. Hillington, opened in 1937, was the first in Scotland and, today, it is the largest of its kind in the whole country. The range of articles made in the estates is astonishing – precision tools and nautical instruments; electric blankets and pressure cookers; Scotch broth (in tins) and sweets; razor blades and refrigerators; clocks and car batteries. Variety of manufacture is an obvious asset – the industrial potential of Scotland is enhanced and an impressive assortment of goods is available for the country's export programme.

A major centre of population. The emergence of the town as an industrial and commercial centre was marked by a rapid increase in the population of Glasgow. Soon after the Act of Union, the population, at the magistrates' census, numbered less than 13,000. Throughout most of the eighteenth century, the increase was very slight. But with the growth of the textile and heavy industries and with the extension of commerce, Glasgow expanded rapidly in all directions. The suburban settlements grew into towns which were, in turn, incorporated within the city boundary. The advance in population was spectacular and each nineteenth-century decennial census showed a substantial increase in the number of people domiciled in the city. The opportunity of employment which Glasgow offered in so many forms drew people from all parts of Scotland.

At the census of 1851, 75 per cent of the population was of Scottish extraction. But at the same census, the proportion of people of Irish birth was no less than 18 per cent of the total population. Dr. Strang, who superintended the enumeration at that time, made the following observations. They are of interest in so far as they reflect the mixed composition of the present population of Glasgow. 'The result of the census appears to be that the Irish [in 1851] bear to the gross population 2·07 per cent more than they did to that of 1841. But this last cipher gives no adequate idea of the increase of those who may be strictly considered as belonging to Ireland, and who are domiciled within the limits of Glasgow and its suburbs. Within the last ten years, the children born here of Irish parents have been very numerous, but these, of course, are all put under the head of Scotch. While, therefore, there appears only to be an increase of 2·07 per cent in the present enumeration, above that which the Irish bore to the population of 1841, the real number of inhabitants who are imbued with Irish characteristics, habits, feelings, and religious sentiments, is infinitely greater.'

A century ago, there were 350,000 people in Glasgow, compared to 84,000 in 1801. By 1901, three-quarters of a million lived in the city and at the last few censuses, the population of Glasgow has been a little over 1 million. The city is by far the largest centre of population in Scotland. The provision of dwelling houses for its populace has long been a problem in Glasgow. Spacious new residential areas, on the outskirts of the city, contain thousands of families. In addition, within recent years, the urban horizon has been transformed by multi-storey buildings, some happily replacing the slum tenements with their dingy backcourts. These huge blocks of flats permit great numbers of people to live in one area. But Glasgow is an overcrowded city. Its so-called 'overspill' plan is designed to attract people to entirely new towns like East Kilbride, Cumbernauld and Livingston or to townships in different parts of Scotland.

3. The Lower Clyde Towns

Downstream from Glasgow, there are several towns which, though similar in type, are smaller in size, population and industrial output. Their nearness to Glasgow does not, however, detract from the importance of the activities of each. In **Paisley (96,000),** a town of great textile renown, massive cotton factories line the White Cart. 'Paisley for cotton thread' is a catch phrase that is appropriate but this is, by no means, the sole industry of the town. Preserves, corn products, soaps, starch, sanitary ware, dyes and machinery along with general engineering give the town an industrial diversity not unlike that of Glasgow.

A Roman camp, on rising ground west of the White Cart, is said to have been an early settlement here. Vanduara, the name given to it, is regarded as a Latin version of the old British words meaning 'White water', the river flowing past the camp on its east side. In the sixth century, several churches were founded in the area by some Irish missionaries among whom was St. Mirren who spent most of his life here. Later, Paisley was important on account of its abbey founded in the twelfth century, and standing close to the White Cart in the centre of the modern town. Soon after the Act of Union, with the advent of the Industrial Revolution, Paisley became a centre of textile manufacture. Bleachfields appeared on the banks of the river and there was plenty of river water at hand for power and processing (dyeing and finishing). It was not long before Paisley developed the manufacture of linen, muslin, cloths mixed with cotton, sewing thread, and silk gauzes.

In the first half of last century, its factories specialised in making imitation Indian and Persian shawls with silk and Cashmere wool. This industry brought great prosperity to Paisley for a time, so much so that the Paisley shawl pattern, an ornamented Indian pine, became distinctive. The Paisley design still survives but the shawl industry fell into decay a century ago due to French competition, to fashion changes and to rivalry from cotton manufacturers. The town suffered a great depression on this account and unemployment was rife in the trade until the invention of the sewing machine, late in the nineteenth century, brought an endless demand for sewing thread. Intricate and technical though the process is which takes cotton strands through a maze of machinery, there emerges, at length, mile after mile of white and coloured thread, tight and compact, on wooden reels or bobbins, which make their way to every corner of the world. Yet the prosperity of the industry springs from the legacy of experience and skill passed on by generations of its textile workers. At Linwood, near Paisley, is a new car factory. From its assembly lines comes a stream of small size cars. At Inchinnan, there is a large tyre factory.

Renfrew (18,000) makes dredgers, hoppers and launches. Its ferry offers an easy crossing of the Clyde. The airport, coping with over a million passengers annually, has been moved to Abbotsinch. There are flights to London, Ireland and the Western Isles. Boilers, cables, animal foods, paints and fuel oil are made in the town.

Clydebank (50,000) is relatively a new town for the two industries which give it world wide fame started here towards the end of last century. In both cases, the difficulty of obtaining suitable space for expansion within Glasgow forced a firm to move to Clydebank. On farmland, with a gentle gradient towards the river, and almost opposite the point where the confluence of the Cart and the Clyde affords additional river space, developed John Brown's ship-building yards. Here have been built some of the largest and best ships of the world – warships, liners, tankers, and tugs. After they have been launched, they go at once to the fitting out basins to be completed by great teams of tradesmen, technicians and engineers. Ship-building keeps many thousands of other workers in employment.

The other industry which gives the town a great reputation is centred in a huge factory whose products are found in every part of the globe. Here are made all sorts and sizes of domestic and industrial sewing machines. Other industries are connected with pumps, steam generators, tools, etc., but shipbuilding and sewing machines account very largely for the rapid rise in population from 10,000 (1891) to 50,000.

Dumbarton (26,000), at the junction of the river Leven and the Clyde, has always had sea connections. Its castle, built on the familiar twin-topped volcanic stump overlooking the main river, was an early fortress and its water front was at one time a Scottish naval base as it had been during the Roman occupation. The town is no longer of strategic importance and, with the closure of its shipyard, the connections with the sea have ceased. There is, however, a large whisky distillery and many are employed in the tube and engineering works. Nearby in the Strathleven Industrial Estate, there are factories in which office equipment is assembled, elastic garments are made and alarm clocks and lenses produced. Alexandria (16,000), in the Vale of Leven, has a torpedo works and a clothing factory. Balloch (2,000) at the end of Loch Lomond and Helensburgh (9,000) near the Gare Loch, are both holiday centres with a great influx of summer visitors.

Greenock, Gourock, and Port Glasgow are separate burghs but, in actual fact, they make up a continuous built-up zone on the south bank of the river Clyde. From fishing hamlets and small seaports, they grew to townships extended along the river front. Their growth is closely associated with local geographical circumstances. It is on the southern bank of the river that the artificially deepened waterway finally clears the river mudbanks and shoals and enters the deep water anchorage at the Tail o' the Bank in the shelter of Greenock Bay. Then as the Renfrew Heights present steep slopes to the river from Port Glasgow all the way round to Inverkip, the narrow rim of the 25 foot raised beach affords restricted space for the towns to grow. Around Port Glasgow and west of Greenock, the raised beach is enclosed by steep sandstone cliff-faces 60-100 feet high. Because the raised beach in the region of Greenock, however, is backed by slopes that are relatively less steep, the town has expanded more easily than its neighbours. Within recent years, Greenock has spread towards and into the Inverkip corridor through which the road and railway run to Wemyss Bay. It is in this direction that the town has its new residential suburbs. Here, too, in the Spango Valley, space is available for industrial development and, already, there is a modern factory which manufactures the latest punch card, time and electronic business equipment.

Although eclipsed by the nineteenth-century development of Glasgow and outrivalled by the deepening of the river, **Greenock**

10

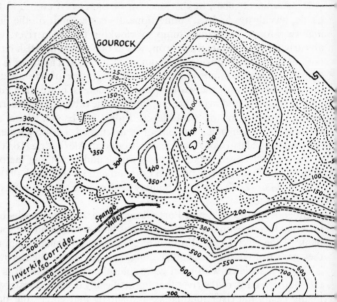

Fig. 54 Gourock, Greenock and Port Gla[s

(75,000) has two main and important industries. Both are attribut-
able to its locational and navigational advantages. For over two
centuries, Greenock has been building ships. Many of them have
come from the famous shipyard of Scotts. Into the deep river
channel, shipwrights of many generations have launched passenger
and cargo vessels, tankers, and warships. Here are craftsmen skilled
in making oil-driven engines, steam turbines and water-tube boilers.
Fortunate in its westerly position, Greenock took full advantage of
the impetus which the Act of Union gave to transatlantic trade.
Imports of sugar cane established the sugar refining industry which
is still a major activity of the town. It is raw sugar which is imported
nowadays from the Caribbean countries and Greenock not only
sends sugar and syrup all over Scotland but carries on a flourishing
export trade.

From ship-building arose the making of ropes, casks and barrels.
Sugar refining encouraged the manufacture of refining machinery

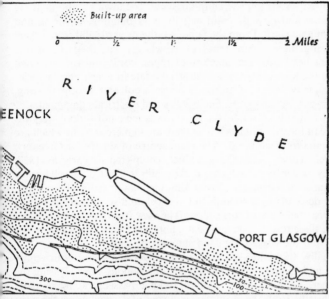

their hinterland (*Crown copyright reserved*)

and sacking. Another mainstay of the town is its woollen industry. High on the hills overlooking the river are the great worsted mills which retail wool and hosiery in every town in Great Britain. The main imports of Greenock are sugar, tobacco, bananas, oilseeds and palm kernels, the last two for making edible fats. Its export trade is in ships. The new large dry dock and repair quay, now in existence in its great harbour, are of immense importance to Greenock and to Clydeside. For the first time on the Clyde, there is a dry dock capable of taking the largest vessels and of providing them with full servicing facilities.

Gourock (9,000), the most western of the Clyde burghs, is very different from its neighbours. It is a most popular holiday resort. Its pier, seldom idle, is used by thousands of holiday-makers and day travellers who use the ferries across the Clyde to places like Dunoon and Rothesay. **Port Glasgow (23,000)** was founded in 1688 and acted as the customs house port of the river before its deepening permitted vessels to proceed to Glasgow. The town's seaborne trade has gone and now its main activity is in building, repairing and breaking up ships. From the famous Lithgow yards and from others adjoining them, many types of vessels are launched. Its textile interest lies in the manufacture of ropes, cords and canvas. High above the town, there is an industrial estate in which new factories make many forms of canvas tentage, wool and cotton shirting, underwear, pyjama wear, fine needles and electrical equipment.

For a supply of water, the three towns have not to look very far afield. In the rain drenched hills there are numerous lochs which are reservoirs for each burgh. The main source of supply for Greenock is Loch Thom. A 5-mile aqueduct, completed as early as 1827, conveys water from the loch round the hills to The Cut, a well known landmark of Greenock. From this high level artificial reservoir, water descends by a conduit to Greenock and several of the town's factories make use of this supply. The view from any vantage point above these towns is magnificent – both the broad panorama of the Firth and the rugged highland summits beyond.

Finally, thousands of visitors and Clydesiders find both enjoyment and interest in an outing on this famous river. During the summer, river steamers, seldom lacking passengers, make daily return trips from the Broomielaw quay in Glasgow down the river to Dunoon, Rothesay and up the Kyles of Bute to Tighnabruaich. The pleasure to be had from good scenery and fine sailing is matched by the unique experience of a close-up view of the Clyde water-front at work – the expanse of docks, the mighty cranes handling the merchandise of vessels lining the quays, the stocks with the steel frames of the ships-to-be, the ferries scurrying across the river, the ploughed fields adjoining the channel, the imposing Dumbarton Rock, the Tail o' the Bank, rendezvous of wartime convoys, and, far down the firth, the silhouette of a merchant vessel, outward bound, a symbol of Glasgow's great commercial links with the rest of the world.

XIV · THE CENTRAL LOWLANDS
THE FORTH VALLEY: FIFE: ANGUS

THE FORTH VALLEY

THE river Forth flows eastwards from Ben Lomond to the North
Sea and its course traverses two thirds of the breadth of Scotland.
Like other important Scottish rivers, its source is not identified by
a single stream but rather by a number of parallel rivulets which
course swiftly down the east slopes of Ben Lomond to form the
Duchray Water. Near Aberfoyle, this hill burn is joined by another
which cascades out of Loch Chon and Loch Ard. Only when the
Duchray Water, thus supplemented, passes beyond Aberfoyle do
maps show it as the river Forth. As such, its course over the short
distance from Aberfoyle to Stirling is very lengthy for, as a finely
graded stream, it twists and turns through the carselands of Menteith. But just before Stirling is reached, the river Teith, fed by
countless burns and lochs in the highlands of southern Perthshire,
joins the river Forth. This is, by far, the largest tributary of the river
Forth. Indeed, at this stage, the river Teith, by virtue of its greater
length and volume, seems more suited to be the parent stream.

Strengthened in this way, the river Forth then passes through
the gap between the Campsie Fells and the Ochil Hills. The drainage
of the latter is gathered up by the river Devon which meanders its
way to the river Forth near Alloa. From Stirling to Alloa, the broad
and level carseland is disrupted as the river Forth stretches its length
by a most remarkable series of loops and erratic turnings. Once
clear of meanders, however, the river begins to assume its estuarine
form and its shore is lined by low raised beaches and long stretches
of sand. At Queensferry, a promontory protruding from the north
shore constricts the breadth of the river to $1\frac{1}{2}$ miles. But, thereafter,
the Firth of Forth expands into a great waterway 20 miles wide as
it merges imperceptibly into the North Sea. Along the firth, on
both sides, the coastal flats are backed by low hills which, even at
their highest in the Moorfoot and Lammermuir Hills, do not rise
much above 1,500 feet. From these ranges drainage systems like
the Water of Leith and the river Esk find an outlet in the Firth of
Forth.

The Upper Forth Valley. The upper portion of the Forth valley is both highland and lowland in character. The low carselands and gently sloping plains of the Forth and the Teith are encircled by highlands, now stern in their bleakness, now majestic in their scenic beauty. This highland zone is not, however, bereft of economic value. Its natural grandeur is enhanced by plantations of young

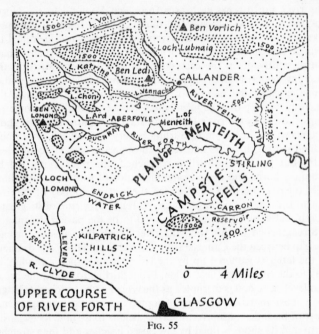

Fig. 55

conifers. The new forests such as at Loch Ard, Aberfoyle and Callander represent part of Scotland's timber programme and at the same time exemplify the adaptation of an apparently unproductive area. In a less direct manner the natural setting, used by Sir Walter Scott for his *Lady of the Lake* and *Rob Roy*, has made the district attractive to tourists; so much so that, every year, thousands of people from all over the world make a point of visiting The Trossachs and the Aberfoyle area. For the angler, too, there is abundant loch and burn fishing in both the Forth and Teith valleys.

Loch Katrine, collecting its waters from a large Highland catchment area, is a natural reservoir from which water is conducted by pipelines to the city of Glasgow. But it is only in these specialised forms that the water resources of the Upper Forth and Teith valleys are utilised. Indeed, had there been local coal measures, the appearance of the Teith valley, with water supplies at hand, might now have been very different.

Agriculture is the mainstay of the lowland community. Especially is this true in the carselands of Menteith. This area forms a sort of natural saucer remarkably flat in the centre. Some inferior boggy land there is but, in general, the riverlands consist of a dark loam which is highly fertile and suited to arable farming. Potato and turnip crops are seen everywhere and oats is the usual grain. The abundant yields of hay and clover show that farming is not, however, confined to arable work. There are herds of Ayrshires, for farms are near enough to centres of demand to warrant dairying. Some grazing is also reserved for store cattle of various breeds. When the outer carseland merges into the broken highlands and the upland slopes of the Campsie Fells, arable farming gives way to rough pasture and the grazing of Blackface flocks becomes the common practice.

The Middle Forth Valley. From the battlements of Stirling Castle, the flat and broad appearance of the carse of Stirling is unmistakable. Its soil varies from stiff clay to more friable loams. In depth, it ranges from several feet nearest the river to a few inches on the rim of the carse. Carse soil is remarkably free of stones and the thin beds of shells which it contains mark the former extent of the Forth estuary. Formerly, because of its low level, the carseland was subject to flooding. But by the construction of flood banks, by the removal of peat, by the installation of an efficient drainage and by deep ploughing, the land was greatly improved.

Early last century, this report was made. 'Thorough draining together with deep and sub-soil ploughing has achieved wonders. It is perfectly wonderful to behold the mighty change this thorough drain system is making . . . wet land is made dry and poor weeping clays are converted into beautiful and rich wheat fields and where the plough could scarcely be driven for slush and water, we now see heavy crops, the quality and quantity alike improved.'

The carse of Stirling has thus been made fit for agriculture and modern mechanical contrivances play their part in maintaining its fertility. That this area is now one of the most productive in Scotland may be attributed, in great measure, to the skill in farm management along with the experience inherited from generations of carseland farmers, accustomed to the heavy texture of their soils. Their fields are level and open to the sun and the rainfall is seldom copious. Such conditions encourage farm activity in all its branches. The carse is excellent crop land. There are substantial crops of oats with some wheat and a little barley. Potatoes are very common and so

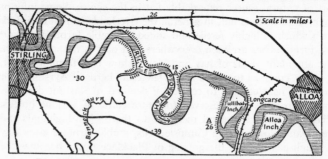

Fig. 56 The loops and carselands of the middle Forth valley
(*Crown copyright reserved*)

are beans which are fed to stock. The production of hay is high, some of it being sold to highland stock rearers. There is good grazing for beef cattle and many farms carry dairy herds. In the Devon valley, conditions are similar. The level fields along the hillfoots are mostly arable. Oats are preferred to wheat and barley. Potatoes again are popular and grass for hay-making occupies a large acreage. Beef and dairy stock are common on the level fields. In contrast, the Ochil Hills, which present a steep scarp face to the riverlands, provide rough pasture for flocks of sheep.

Farming activities, however, have been restricted by coal mining. The low country around the head of the estuary contains rich seams. The collieries are easily discernible by their large winding wheels and by the refuse bings. In Stirling and Clackmannanshire, coal mining has long been important. The principal collieries are near Stirling – Manor Powis, Polmaise and Bannockburn. In the Ochil hillfoots, coal is mined at Dollar. Further down the firth, at Bo'ness, the Kinneil colliery is a very important unit.

But the town of **Stirling (28,000)** is not a centre of industrial importance. It stands in the gap between the Ochil Hills and the Campsie Fells and its site, formerly of great strategic value, now furnishes it with a rôle like that of Perth. Prior to the construction of the Kincardine (1936) and Forth (1964) road bridges, Stirling was the last road-crossing point before the widening of the estuary. Even so, it is still a focal point of routes. Both road and rail communications pass through it and radiate in every direction. Its location amidst excellent farming country makes it a convenient market centre and an attractive shopping centre.

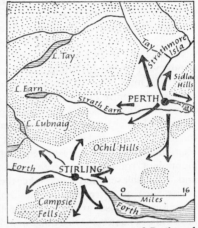

FIG. 57 The route centres of Perth and Stirling

The new University will add still further to its regional importance.

Alloa (14,000), its neighbour, is more engrossed in industry. Its engineering is concerned with pump, hydraulic and electrical machinery. There are paper and woollen yarn factories, the town having formerly some reputation in the manufacture of plaidings and tartans. Its present importance centres on two products which, like its textile activities, have been associated with it for a very long time. Its breweries produce great amounts of high quality draught and bottled beer. Both find a ready market in the industrial areas of Scotland and northern England. The breweries also cater for a substantial overseas demand and, despite Danish and German competition, Alloa beer is still shipped to tropical countries from Glasgow and Leith. Glass making has been carried on in the town for two centuries. Its works produce a variety of glassware mainly for Scottish industries, milk, beer and particularly whisky bottles as well as modern food jars and containers. Sand – a raw material of the industry – was once found locally. Now some comes from West Lothian but most silver sands are shipped from Belgium.

Neither Stirling nor Alloa have the industrial and commercial importance of Falkirk and Grangemouth. **Falkirk (38,000),** once noted as a great trysting place or focus of the cattle trade of Scotland, is now a very busy manufacturing centre. Local supplies of coal and ironstone first induced Dr. Roebuck, a Sheffield physician, to start an iron works at Carron as early as 1760. The industry was, in effect, a product of the Industrial Revolution and all sorts of cast iron goods were made including instruments of war. Although raw materials must now be obtained from outside sources, Falkirk remains the centre of the modern cast-iron trade and its foundries turn out baths, cookers (electric and gas), grates, pipes, telephone kiosks and pillar boxes. The aluminium industry is a recent development in the town. It dates from the last war when great quantities of aluminium alloy sheeting were required for aircraft production. The aluminium rolling mills receive aluminium from Fort William and Kinlochleven and undertake the production of aluminium pieces such as corrugated aluminium, strip aluminium for constructional purposes as well as long rolls of sheet and strip aluminium. Falkirk has a very wide range of industries. Brewing is important and other activities include coach building and road haulage, book binding and printing, chemicals and timber.

At Bonnybridge (6,000), the presence of fireclay accounts for the manufacture of refractory bricks used in fireplaces, stoves, furnaces and foundries. Cumbernauld, a new town, has been created to take part of Glasgow's overspill population and to attract new industries. (See Chapter XVIII p. 243).

Less than five miles from Falkirk and on the estuary of the river Forth is the town of **Grangemouth (19,000).** Geographical position has always favoured Grangemouth. Its original function was as the eastern outlet of the Forth-Clyde canal. The canal is no longer in existence but Grangemouth still remains an important port. It lies well upstream and convenient road and rail routes place it within easy access of the manufacturing areas of Central Scotland. In particular, its hinterland stretches across to the industrial centres of the lower Clyde valley. Today it is an important centre of commerce, especially well located for trade with North European lands. The port handles a large tonnage and a great variety of export and import commodities. Its export list includes most of the products made in Central Scotland. Its import trade is still greater in value.

The main cargoes discharged are all essentials such as crude oil, timber, esparto grass, paper, iron ore, etc.

The production and refining of oils from shales mined in West Lothian prompted the installation of an oil refinery at Grangemouth. A considerable quantity of crude oil is now discharged from large tankers at Finnart on Loch Long and then pumped across to Grangemouth through a pipeline 57 miles long. The oil is processed into main products like petrol, paraffin, fuel oils and gas. There is sufficient level land alongside the river Forth for the storage of oil in massive tanks prior to distribution. Grangemouth is the main oil refining centre of Scotland.

Oil refining has led to petro-chemicals. Petroleum derivatives are passed as 'feedstock' to the town's chemical plants which employ highly technical processes to produce dyes, soaps and detergents, basic elements for paints, varnishes, insecticides, plastics as well as polybutadiene (i.e. synthetic rubber), so essential in vehicle, footwear and other industries. Grangemouth is one of the greatest petro-chemical centres of Great Britain.

No large scale production of iron, oil and chemicals is possible without an accessible supply of water. Both Falkirk and Grangemouth are within a short distance of a cluster of lochs tucked in small upland basins in the Campsie Fells. The lochs, fed by many a hill burn, are utilised as storage reservoirs. The largest is the Carron Valley reservoir at an elevation of 600 feet. The water is brought down by pipeline to the two towns.

The Lower Forth Valley. Along the south shore of the Firth of Forth lie the three Lothian counties. The Pentland, Moorfoot, and Lammermuir Hills, a long east-west stretch of uplands, make a suitable boundary to the region. The southern part of West Lothian is a mixture of boggy moorland and upland waste which provides a contrast to the low and level riverlands of the Forth estuary. The drainage of the county is insignificant except for the river Avon which is the county's western boundary for most of its course.

In Midlothian, the general south-north inclination is repeated. The most prominent hills are the Pentland Hills which reach 1,800 feet on the county border. They descend gradually towards the plain of the river Forth. In and around Edinburgh the low riverlands and links are interrupted by small hill groups like the Corstorphine and Braid Hills or by steep summits like Arthur's Seat and Salisbury

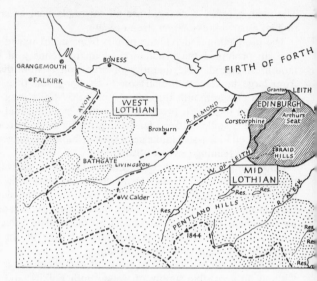

FIG. 58

Crags, the Calton Hill and the Castle Rock. The Pentland Hills are
furrowed by numerous burns which make their way into the two
major rivers of Midlothian. Both follow courses which are roughly
parallel and their direction of flow is north-eastwards. The Water
of Leith winds and twists round the west and north of Edinburgh
to the Port of Leith. The waters of the North and South Esk, joining
below Dalkeith, empty into the river Forth by a shallow estuary.
The lochs which appear in the courses of many hill burns are used as
reservoirs of water for supplying nearby Edinburgh. The Moorfoot
Hills, lying to the south-east of Midlothian, contain similar reservoirs, but the major source for the Edinburgh area lies in the Talla
reservoir of the upper Tweed basin.

In East Lothian, the Lammermuir Hills rise to the height of
1,750 feet in the south of the county. They descend to the easily
graded valley of the river Tyne. Beyond, a low range, seen best in
the Garleton Hills at Haddington, intervenes before the land drops
to the low Forth coastlands. North Berwick Law (613 feet), a volcanic stump visible for miles around, rears up above the plain. A

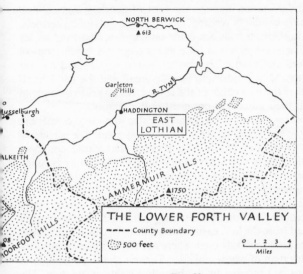

NORTH BERWICK
▲ 613

Garleton
Hills
R. TYNE

usselburgh

HADDINGTON
EAST
LOTHIAN

ALKEITH

LAMMERMUIR HILLS
▲1750

THE LOWER FORTH VALLEY
---- County Boundary
500 feet

0 1 2 3 4
Miles

OORFOOT HILLS

Fig. 58

great network of rills and hill torrents course down from the
Lammermuir Uplands. They feed the river Tyne and other lesser
rivers. Their direction of flow is not to the river Forth but to the
east, i.e. into the North Sea.

Despite the encroachment of mining and industry, good use is
made of the land for farming. Food production is customary in
Lothian farms but the rearing of livestock is not ousted altogether
by arable cropping. Broad stretches of level or gently sloping
shorelands with fine carse and loamy soils are obvious benefits to
farming. So also are abundant sunshine and great economic demand.
There is, too, plenty of rough hill pasture. But to these assets must
be added other influences to account for the high standard of farming
in the area. The improvement in farming practices which emerged
with the agricultural revolution of the last two centuries was given
great encouragement by the activities of the Edinburgh agricultural
societies. For over 150 years, also, there have been agricultural classes
at the University of Edinburgh and over the same period, Edinburgh
printing presses have been producing texts on agricultural procedure.

In more modern times, there is the East of Scotland Agricultural College which conducts research and provides advice to farmers.

In West Lothian, cereals are commonly grown. Oats and barley have a similar acreage, and a little wheat is grown. Main crops of ware potatoes are lifted every year as well as turnips and hay for winter fodder. Milk production is widespread and the dairy herds far outnumber the beef cattle of the county. Sheep graze the upland pastures but their number is not great in this county.

In Midlothian, which is far greater in size, the same cereals are grown but the acreage of each grain is twice as great. The acreage in potatoes, turnips and hay is also greater. Beef cattle are more numerous than dairy cows. About one-third of the county is rough pasture and flocks are common particularly on the southern hills and even on pastures in the vicinity of Edinburgh.

In East Lothian, the farmlands facing the Forth estuary carry cereals and roots. The district is intensely cultivated. Extremely good yields are had from the low, easily worked fields in which mechanical contrivances are commonly used. There is, overall, a greater production of barley than of wheat and oats. Turnips and sugar beet, both heavier crops, are eclipsed by the bountiful yields of potatoes. The red soils of the Dunbar district are of repute for potato cultivation. Throughout East Lothian, dairying is important but the numbers of beef cattle are greater. In the south of the county there is mixed farming with sheep flocks more frequent than cattle stock. In the remote Lammermuir Hills, hill farms predominate and there is ample grazing for sheep on the great stretches of rough pasture and heather.

The extraordinary emphasis on market gardening in the Lothians merits special mention. A very large proportion of all the vegetables grown for human consumption in Scotland comes from market gardens in this area. The market garden belt extends coastwise from Linlithgow to Dunbar and along the river valleys such as those of the Esk and Tyne. Almost every sort of vegetable is grown – cabbages, brussels sprouts, turnips, cauliflowers, peas, beetroot, lettuce, and onions. Dalkeith is well noted for green vegetables and so is Musselburgh which is also famous for its leek crop. Throughout the Lothians, the growing of tomatoes and lettuces under glass is another important activity and the three counties have the largest area of glasshouses and frames in Scotland. In acreage devoted to vegetables, no other county exceeds East Lothian.

The Lothians owe this superiority in horticulture mainly to situation and soil type. On the raised beaches fringing the river Forth the soils are of a light type and in the river bottoms there is fine alluvial soil. Many nurseries are also favoured by a fair degree of shelter along with much sunshine. Most important, too, are the numerous towns in central Scotland with their enormous demand (summer and winter) for fresh green vegetables. The Lothian market gardeners not only cater for the nearby Edinburgh market and central Scotland but also send consignments as far as Newcastle.

But, besides all these advantages, the area is one with traditions of good husbandry. There are records of horticultural activity long ago in the Lothians. As early as the twelfth and thirteenth centuries, the area contained many large gardens and orchards, tended, most likely, by monks well versed in fruit husbandry. David I, a skilled horticulturist, was known to have had a large garden under the Castle Rock of Edinburgh. In a map of old Edinburgh, dated 1647, spacious gardens appear at the back of the large houses in the Royal Mile. Commercial horticulture in the Lothians may thus be traced back to such early efforts at land utilisation.

The Lothian coalfield, situated on the south side of the firth, contains a plentiful supply of coal. The coalfield is small in area but very rich in coal measures. It lies to the east of Edinburgh and extends from Tranent through Dalkeith to the Penicuik district. The coal area is in the nature of a basin, with a north to south axis. The most valuable seams lie concealed at great depth in the centre of the basin and there are coal measures under the Firth of Forth. Around Bathgate, a group of West Lothian coalpits forms an important section of the Central coalfield.

As in other coal areas of the Forth, the mining of coal in the Lothians can be traced back several centuries. There is still a great reserve of deep-seated coals. The current programme of reconstruction entails the installation of labour saving and speedy haulage devices. The present output of the Lothians area is over 3 million tons per annum. Collieries which make an important contribution are located at Bilston Glen, Loanhead, Monktonhall near Dalkeith and Newtongrange. Their shafts, at 1,500-3,000 feet, reach deep and rich seams. With the city of Edinburgh as its economic hub, the Lothians area is serving the needs of local industries. Moreover, the new Cockenzie power station will depend on a regular, substantial supply of Lothian coal. At its fullest development, it will absorb about 3 million tons per year. Monktonhall colliery will supply over a million tons of crushed coal annually and the rest will be provided by Bilston Glen and other local pits.

The Lower Forth valley is no longer noted for shale mining. The red tabular bings that remain belong to the past. The prosperity of West Lothian lies in the emergence of new industries. They provide work for men and women residing within and furth of the county. The factories have an advantageous location – close to the A8, convenient for Glasgow and Edinburgh and not far from Grangemouth or the new Forth bridge. At Broxburn (10,000), factories produce potato crisps, heating plant and transformers, as well as synthetic thread. Bathgate is the other of the two main centres of the Scottish motor vehicle industry. Its new factory, its large workshops and spacious vehicle compounds, easily visible from the A8, assembles tractors, trucks and vans for home and overseas markets. Both for bringing components to the factory, e.g. steel from Ravenscraig or cabins from Linwood, and for distributing the finished vehicles, the location of the factory on a major road-way, is especially favourable. Livingston, near Edinburgh and the latest of Scotland's new towns, is designed to accommodate 100,000 people and to attract new industries. (See Chapter XVIII pp 243). At Bo'ness (10,000), noted for its Kinneil colliery, there are plans for new light engineering factories.

Edinburgh (468,000). Edinburgh, capital of Scotland and second largest city, possesses an individuality that is undeniably supreme. Throughout its long and, at times, turbulent history, the city has extended progressively to the lowlands far beyond the Castle Rock. Its original site and function were not geographical accidents. The earliest settlers sought a suitable place of refuge on the familiar summit of the Castle Rock, one of several hills which overshadow the modern city. With its precipitous sides, this volcanic stump had a natural advantage as it assured a measure of protection on three sides at least.

From this settlement there emerged the medieval township which developed in an easterly direction beyond the precincts of the castle. Its expansion was at first the direct result of physical circumstances and later that of human expediency. The long trail of glacial debris, from the castle along the Royal Mile down to the surrounding lowland, marks the general line of the streets and buildings of old Edinburgh. The town, increasing in size and population, was both the seat of parliament and a royal abode, rôles which it shared with several other Scottish towns. When, on his accession in 1437, James II preferred Edinburgh as his residence and as the seat of government, its status as capital of Scotland became permanent. At the Union of the Crowns, Edinburgh had no longer a royal court in continuous residence and at the Act of Union, parliaments forsook Edinburgh for London but its administrative function is still deepy rooted.

As the capital, Edinburgh is now the centre of public administration in Scotland – legal, educational, medical, agricultural, etc. Administration is, in effect, a major activity of the city and a good proportion of its populace finds employment in the numerous offices of national and private concerns. Similarly, by virtue of its status, Edinburgh is a celebrated banking and insurance centre. The principal banking and insurance establishments of Scotland have their headquarters in Edinburgh from which are controlled the activities of their branches located all over Scotland and beyond.

Fig. 59 Section from an old map showing courts and gardens in the Royal Mile, Edinburgh in the mid-seventeenth century.

Although the modern city extends to the Forth waterfront, it is the Old Town that remains supreme in historic interests. The High Street and the Canongate, more familiar as the Royal Mile, St. Giles Cathedral, and the Palace of Holyroodhouse are some of the treasures of old Edinburgh. Most conspicuous of all is the Castle which, as a citadel, now crowns the modern city and towers over Princes Street. This, the main highway of the capital, consists, on

11

its north side, of a long, grand terrace with attractive shops and hotels. Its fine buildings and those of the stately squares and streets behind it provide a contrast to the closely built Old Town and lend a dignity to this newer part of Edinburgh which dates mainly from the eighteenth century. On the other side of Princes Street, its gardens which may be said to divide old from new Edinburgh, lie below the Castle Rock. Its spacious flower beds and grassy slopes were formerly occupied by an ill-drained lake, the North Loch.

For its fine setting Edinburgh is famous; for its impressive buildings, it is likewise renowned and for its historic interest, the capital is unique in Scotland. But now through its annual Festival of Art, Drama, and Music, started in 1947, the city has experienced a very rapid increase in its attractiveness. The very large number of people who visit Edinburgh in summer and at other times of the year is proof enough of its importance as a cultural and tourist centre.

Indeed, such is its reputation in this respect that the industrial activities of Edinburgh are often overlooked. Its manufactures are most varied but the industrial pattern is not like that of Glasgow. The textile, ship-building, and engineering industries, for example, so much a part of the life of Clydeside, have anything but an exact counterpart in Edinburgh. Even so, its industries are, by no means, insignificant. Printing and publishing are two of the foremost industries. The cultural outlook of the capital is a strong reason for their location and development. Soon after Caxton introduced his printing press to London, there was a press in Edinburgh for printing legal and parliamentary papers as well as educational and religious books. But this early trade is not to be compared to the huge expansion of printing in the city in the second half of the eighteenth and in the early years of the nineteenth century. Then the literary achievements of Scotsmen like Ramsay, Smollett, Ferguson, Burns, and Scott stimulated an extraordinary demand for their works and Edinburgh soon acquired a world renown for its books and journals.

The existence of the University, founded in 1582, and of many celebrated schools and colleges, the presence of the Law Courts, government and commercial offices, all helped to foster the printing of a great assortment of textbooks and maps by a group of well-established firms. The printing industry is supplied with paper made in and near Edinburgh. The paper mills, located on the river Esk and the Water of Leith, are dependent on their water supply. Wood pulp from Scandinavia and esparto grass from North Africa are imported in great quantities to keep the mills going. Many types of paper are produced, particularly high quality paper for various uses.

The location of the brewing industry in the city has been due to the presence of water, suitable for brewing, in the sandstones of Edinburgh. Thanks to this water supply, obtained from deep wells in the city, the brewing industry has acquired a high reputation. The export of its Scotch ales confirms the popularity of Edinburgh beer in every part of the world. Home grown barley from the neighbouring counties is not sufficient to meet the requirements of the score of breweries in the city and foreign barley is imported through the Port of Leith. With such a reliable source of water and with a plentiful supply of grain, it is not surprising that the largest distilleries of Scotland are located in the city. Because of its position, Edinburgh is an important distributing centre in the whisky trade.

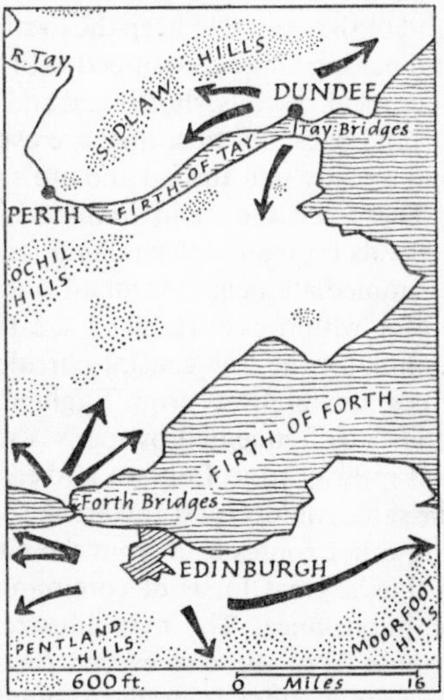

FIG. 60 The route centres of Dundee and Edinburgh

Edinburgh is a major centre of rubber production. This industry started in the city over a century ago on the initiative of an American firm. Since its birth, the industry has experienced enormous expansion due, mainly, to the adaptability of rubber to the modern techniques of the industrial world. The Edinburgh mills manufacture many tough, durable products – tyres, belting, hose and thermoplastic sheets.

Since 1943, the city has had a modern electronic industry. Several thousands of highly trained personnel are now employed at the large factory at Crewe Toll making electronic devices associated with air navigation. Electrical engineering (rotating plant connected with switch and control gear) is also well established and the manufacture of ocean liner stabilisers makes marine engineering noteworthy. Nucleonic equipment for the detection of radiation is yet another new, important item of manufacture. Such industries are a complete contrast to the old-established activities and give emphasis to the modern trend of industrial growth in Edinburgh.

In contrast, the modern baking and milling industries had their roots in the district. There were supplies of grain in the rich hinterland of the capital to keep the local mills busy. But now the great mills and baking houses, equipped with up-to-date mechanical plant, produce meal, biscuits, shortbread and confectionery. Packed in attractive tartan boxes and tins, they are ever popular with visitors. They also find a ready sale abroad and are a most valuable export of Scotland.

These are the main industries of Edinburgh and their success depends on many inter-related factors. The rich agricultural land in its immediate neighbourhood has been noted. There is a source of power within easy reach in the Lothian coalfield. But the city also dominates the low coastal corridor of the Border route. In earlier times, this highway from England through Edinburgh to the Highlands was frequented by many a military force. Now the main road and railway from London and eastern England reach the city along the same route. Good and quick routes link Edinburgh and Glasgow and other routes lead from the city to central Scotland. Edinburgh is thus a great focus of communications and a distributing centre of importance. The map illustrates this well. The routes which radiate from the city exceed those of Dundee but the pattern of communications is similar though reversed in orientation.

Roads and railways spread out fanwise from Edinburgh. The older Forth railway bridge is now partnered by the new road bridge. With the completion of the new Tay road bridge at Dundee, road communications from the capital have been wholly transformed. Edinburgh has now direct north-south road links with the whole of the east of Scotland, an immediate convenience to both private and commercial road users.

The Port of Leith, part of Edinburgh since 1920, has an advantageous position on account of its access and nearness to Northern Europe. Much of its trade, overall relatively small, is with countries across the North Sea. With more distant continents, it conducts an important trade in grain from the Americas, Africa and Australasia. Coastal shipping routes serve the northern isles and London but Leith acts more as a port for Edinburgh and Central Scotland. Imports are far more important than exports. The principal imports are grains (wheat, barley, maize), fertilisers, timber, paper, pulp, cement and dairy produce. Its exports, significantly declining over recent decades, are of general cargo, e.g. coal (far less than formerly), iron and steel, flour, meal, animal food, beer and paper. There is a Dock Development Scheme which will reconstruct its docks. By infilling, reclamation and deepening, Leith is to be made a deep water port, capable of admitting ships of 40-50,000 tons at all tides. Leith has considerable industry. Besides rope-making, there is ship-building on a small scale. Fertilisers are made and there are several biscuit factories. Distilling and flour milling are both carried on. Newhaven and Granton are the most important fishing ports of the Firth of Forth. Haddock and whiting are the principal fish landed by trawler at the nearby port of Granton.

This account may serve to illustrate the salient factors which affect the growth of a large city. The cultural and tourist outlook of the capital stands out more vividly than its industrial purpose. But, as it is today, Edinburgh is, in effect, the outcome of a long and complex combination of geological, geographical, and social influences.

Musselburgh (18,000), a three bridge town at the mouth of the river Esk, has a reputation for golf and horse racing, its nearness to Edinburgh being much in its favour in this connection. The town is not without industry. One factory, with over 1,000 workers, special-ises in the manufacture of many kinds of wire. Fishing nets and lines are made and there is a paper mill. North Berwick is attractive to visitors and so is Dunbar. Both contain 4,000 people but, in the summertime, they cater for many holiday-makers. Dunbar is also important for its limestone quarry and cement works. Haddington, another small town, stands on the river Tyne. Its central position befits its rôle as a county town. It is a market centre for the local farming area but there are knitwear, tweed, and flour mills in the town.

FIFE

The peninsular county of Fife, in the middle of the east Central Lowlands, has a general undulating outline. Overall, the county does

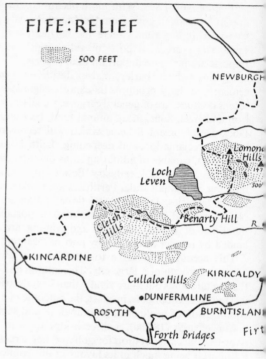

FIG. 61

not rise much above 500 feet. Its bolder landforms reach their highest along its western border. They are extensions of the Ochil Hills and consist of three arms or ridges of low hills. In the north, the hills of Fife overlook the river Tay. Another hill group extends eastwards from the Lomond Hills, with their steep northern face, through central Fife almost to the East Neuk. In a similar way, more low hills cut across the southern part of the county in the direction of Burntisland.

The hills encircle rivers which drain eastwards but are not great in size. The rivers Ore and Leven traverse uneven land but the river Eden passes through the flat basin of the Howe of Fife. Raised beaches, long and level, appear on the coastal fringe of the county;

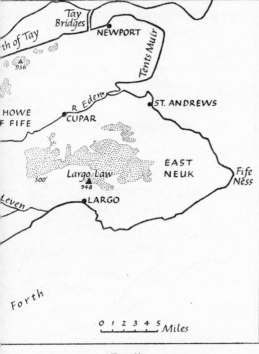

FIG. 61

they are particularly noticeable in the links of St. Andrews as well as along the shore of the Firth of Forth.

Despite its great industrial development, the agricultural activities of Fife are worthy of mention. The county does not possess the definite agricultural belts which are well recognised in Perthshire and Angus, yet its light rainfall and abundance of summer sunshine have encouraged farmers to make their land productive and to keep it highly fertile. Farming is mainly, but seldom exclusively, arable. The local topography and soil type have a great bearing on the character of the farming pursuits. The sandy loams of the Howe of Fife and the lighter soils of the level lands of the East Neuk are part of the highly productive and prosperous 'Golden Fringe' of the

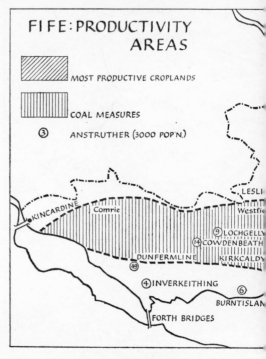

FIG. 62

county. The western hilly parts with their heavier soils are less productive than the coastal strips. Although the land does not rise very high in Fife, cultivation is not easy in fields with a steepish gradient.

Much land is devoted to the production of grain crops. Today, the predominant cereal is barley but wheat is widely grown and so also are oats. Everywhere, potatoes enjoy great popularity while turnips and beans are grown in great quantities for stock feeding. But the arable coastal fringe excepted, mixed farming is the common practice on most farms. Not only do farmers grow cereal and root crops but they also allot a good proportion of their land to grass as summer pasture with hay for winter indoor feeding. Beef cattle

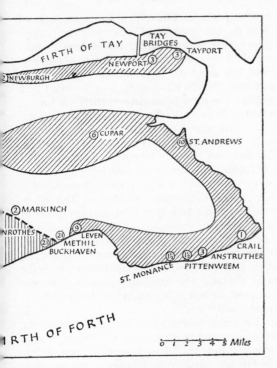

FIG. 62

outnumber dairy herds but the increasing demands for milk and meat products, particularly the former, make stock raising a profitable activity. There is little room for fruit cultivation save for some raspberry plantations. But sugar beet, grown on some of the best arable land, is very important. It is a bulky farm product entailing heavy work in lifting for which a good supply of labour is required late in the year. The beet is sent to the sugar factory at Cupar.

The county derives its economic importance from its industrial rather than from its farming activities. Fife has been fortunate in having an enduring supply of coal. For many a century it was worked in a simple way and was used, in early times, as a domestic fuel. During the last two centuries, Fife coal, in seams not far from the surface, has been the raw material of industry in the county. The collieries in the Cowdenbeath-Lochgelly district were responsible for a large part of all the coal extracted in Fife. Now this part is not important but Fife continues to be a major contributor to Scotland's supply of coal. Despite pit closures, over 3 million tons are produced annually. The most productive districts are (*a*) the coastal strip from Kirkcaldy to Methil (Scotland's chief coal exporting port); (*b*) the east-west section of the river Ore from Kelty to Dundonald and (*c*) the district along the Forth close to Kincardine. Here, the Valleyfield pit is now linked by a tunnel under the Forth to Kinneil colliery, Bo'ness. The Glenrothes colliery, hitherto prominent, has ceased operations but a new one is now in production at Seafield, Kirkcaldy. North of this town, at Michael (Dysart), is Scotland's largest colliery, with an output of several thousands of tons daily. With shafts reaching deep-seated coals and with modern mechanisation, Fife provides about a fifth of Scotland's output. Kincardine electricity power station (and its neighbour-to-be, at Longannet) draws on coal from nearby pits which also supply the carbonising plant at Comrie. The Lurgi gas plant at Westfield depends on local coal and the new power station on the foreshore at Methil uses slurry (soft coal waste).

The county thus has ample coal at hand. To a lesser extent, the rivers of the county, in normal years, provide a useful amount of water needed in industry. But, apart from these two essentials, the major industries in Fife are sustained by supplies of raw materials from sources outside the county. Inevitably transport services perform an extremely vital function in industrial production; the peninsular nature of the county renders this factor even more emphatic. Hitherto, the county has suffered the distinct disadvantage of inadequate 'through' road communication. Now, the Tay and Forth road and rail bridges provide direct crossings into and out of the county. The new bridges will be of even greater economic value when joined up by highways passing through the centre of the county. In Fife, good communications and industrial prosperity are mutually related.

One of the main industries of the county is the manufacture of textiles. It is by no means a new industry nor has its character remained unchanged. As in many parts of Scotland, a few centuries ago, flax growing was common in Fife. The crop was as poor as the state of agriculture then was. But soon after the Act of Union grants were provided to improve the flax crop, particularly the flax seed. Financial help too was available, for example, through the newly formed British Linen Bank, to assist manufacturers in marketing their linen goods outside Scotland.

By the middle of the eighteenth century, the rural village of **Dunfermline** was becoming a thriving centre for the manufacture of table linens. As a very early royal residence, established on a low plateau above the river Forth, Dunfermline was also well known as the site of an abbey founded in the eleventh century. But once its linen manufactures found favour outside Scotland, the town became the principal linen producing centre of Fife and indeed of Scotland. Dunfermline's association with the linen industry has never ceased, yet the emphasis in its textile production has been transformed. Despite a decrease in the popular demand for linen, pillow cases and tablecloths and such like are still made. Far more important, however, are the new fabrics and synthetic fibres like nylon, as well as pure silk. The new textiles are in many forms – dress and tie fabrics, children's wear, skirts and lingerie, in a very wide range of colours and patterns. Along with tarpaulins and conveyor belts, they account for much of the present industrial activity in Dunfermline (49,000).

The other important textile centre is **Kirkcaldy (53,000)** with a similar history in the manufacture of linen cloth. Household linen is made as well as the heavier linen and cotton products such as furnishing fabrics, tenting and canvas. But the industry for which Kirkcaldy is now world famous is the manufacture of linoleum. Its development in Scotland is attributed to Michael Nairn who, in the middle of last century, began to produce floorcloth with a canvas base. This was a vast improvement on the waxcloth floor covering then in use and the industry started to flourish in Kirkcaldy. Today, its two great firms produce the greater part of the linoleum made in Great Britain (the word linoleum is now used in place of floorcloth). In composition, durability, and colour effects, the high quality linoleum of Kirkcaldy is a vast improvement on Nairn's first floorcloth. Both at home and abroad, the demand is at a very high level and it is one of the most valuable exports of Scotland.

The raw materials for its manufacture are brought to Kirkcaldy from distant sources. The backing for the linoleum is no longer of flax canvas but of jute grown in East Pakistan and, most likely, made up at Dundee's jute factories. On to the backing goes cork which is obtained from the bark of the cork oak grown in Portugal. Linseed oil, also used in its manufacture, is derived from the seeds of the flax plant. This is transported to Kirkcaldy in tankers from North and South America. An extension of the manufacturing technique of the industry is the use of rubber, wood flour, felt and paper in the production of very modern types of floor coverings. Kirkcaldy also makes carpets and has a large furniture factory. A new factory is engaged in producing telephonic apparatus.

Paper manufacture is yet another industry of Fife dependent on raw materials from abroad. Guardbridge on the river Eden near St. Andrews, Leslie and Leven are three centres of manufacture. In addition to home supplies of rags, rope, and waste paper, the mills require regular shipments of wood pulp from Scandinavia and esparto grass from North Africa. The finished products range from fine paper and envelopes to paper bags and sacks.

Burntisland (6,000) is a centre for the aluminium industry. The raw material from which aluminium is obtained is bauxite. It is a whitish-grey or reddish-brown mineral, so called because it was discovered originally at Les Baux in southern France. France has ceased to be the chief source of supply. Burntisland now receives high grade bauxite in quantity from Ghana. Only the first stage of the industry, the processing of bauxite, takes place at Burntisland. Pure alumina, a whitish powder, is extracted from the bauxite and the waste residue – iron oxide – is now deposited behind the town. The alumina is sent off by rail to the Highlands where, at Ft. William and Kinlochleven, it is transformed, by electrolytic processes, into aluminium ingots. These in turn go to the aluminium rolling mills at Falkirk.

Ship-building is also carried on at Burntisland. The industry is relatively small in size. The productive capacity of the shipyards is not now above a few thousand tons per annum and the launching programme for one year does not exceed five vessels. Small cargo boats are usually built, diesel driven and mostly of British 'registration. In the small towns around the Fife coast, the construction of lighter craft like launches and fishing boats provides a means of employment and helps to sustain the precarious fishing industry at such small ports as Anstruther (3,000) (nowadays white fish) and Crail (lobsters and crabs), a small picturesque village of the East Neuk. Rosyth, on the landward side of the Forth Bridge, is a famous naval base at which the repair and maintenance of ships of the Royal Navy is undertaken. At Inverkeithing (4,000), there are paper mills and a ship-breaking yard.

Glenrothes (16,000),* second of Scotland's new towns, has experienced a rapid growth of population since 1948. Its population will at length be double this figure, with an overspill of 6,000 from Glasgow. Despite the closure of its colliery, the town has achieved a wide diversity of industrial output. To the established paper and blanket industries, its three new industrial estates have added a great variety of manufactures. Many are ultra-modern, of a scientific nature and capable of substantial growth. The products vary from transistors, electronic and hydraulic components, to papermaking and mining machinery, turbo-generator parts, plastic sports goods, wire baskets and ladies clothing. With factory space, accessible ports and a steady rise in population, Glenrothes is capable of further expansion.

Cupar (6,000), a market town on the river Eden, has the only sugar-beet factory in Scotland and at the small town of Markinch, there is a paper mill and a distillery.

One other occupation which provides work, especially of a seasonal character, is that of catering for great numbers of holidaymakers who are attracted to coastal resorts like Aberdour, Leven, and Crail. But **St. Andrews (9,000),** whose university founded in 1411 is the oldest in Scotland, is the most popular holiday centre. Its broad stretch of golden sands extends the whole length of the raised beach as far as the wooded tracts of Tentsmuir. To its championship golf courses come thousands of golfers every year from all parts of the world.

Favourable climate, productive farmland, abundant coal resources, variety of industrial output, attractive holiday facilities, these furnish a substantial summary of the economic geography of the county of Fife.

*(Estimated 1964.)

ANGUS, KINCARDINE,
AND SOUTH EAST PERTHSHIRE

This geographical region is the north-east section of the Central Lowlands. Most of it lies in Angus and Kincardine but the south-east parts of Perthshire are included. The area can be divided into several well-marked zones of contrasting relief. First, the Highland edge of the Central Lowlands delimits the region on its landward side. Then there is the syncline or trough of Strathmore. It is separated from the low Carse of Gowrie and the Angus-Kincardine coastlands by the Sidlaw Hills.

The rivers which cross the area on their way to the North Sea have their sources in the adjacent Highlands. They descend abruptly as hill burns through narrow and picturesque glens to the floor of Strathmore. Both the North Esk and South Esk wind slowly across Strathmore to the North Sea but their headstreams are swift highland torrents as they plunge through the lovely Glens of Esk, Clova, and Prosen. The main river of Strathmore is the Isla which, after it drops to the strath, is fed by burns that hasten through Glen Shee and Strathardle. In turn, the river Isla drains to the river Tay which, as it emerges from its long narrow strath, makes an abrupt change of direction and bends southwards to Perth. Rivers Almond and Earn, as right bank tributaries, pass through open valleys before they join the river Tay, the one above, the other below Perth. In its lower course, the river Tay continues eastwards through its long firth to the North Sea.

The Highland Edge. The line of the Highland edge is interrupted at several points by the deep and very beautiful glens of the rivers descending to Strathmore. Their valley floors are dotted by scattered and remote farmsteads set in ploughlands and pasture with sheep grazings reaching up the steep slopes of the glens. At the points where the glens open on to Strathmore, there are several small towns like Blairgowrie (5,000) and Kirriemuir (3,500). Their site is significant. They are market centres and much road traffic is drawn to them. Agricultural engineering and milling are carried on.

Strathmore. Strathmore stretches roughly from Perth north-eastwards to Brechin. It is a shallow groove bounded by the ramparts of the Highlands and by the more smooth northern slopes of the Sidlaw Hills. For the most part, it is below 200 feet, gentle in contour and at times very level. Along the floor of the strath, tributaries like the Isla pursue a tortuous course and find an outlet to the river Tay and the river Esk. Its soils consist of free-working loam and deep alluvium but there are tracts of stiff clay.

The strath is a most productive area. It is noted for the breeding of pedigree stock and for arable farming. A great variety of crops

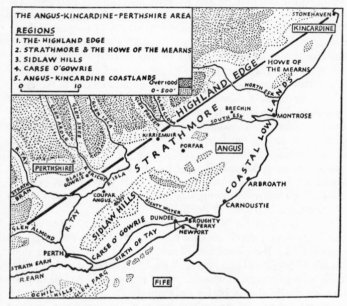

FIG. 63

is grown. Apart from the common cereals and sugar beet, special attention is given to potato growing. Main crops, sown throughout March and April and lifted in October, are the chief source of income on many farms. Strathmore seed potatoes, good in yield and quality, are world famous. There is a keen demand in Scotland for the Kerr's Pink and Majestic varieties but growers also send consignments of Majestic and King Edwards to England and to a number of countries overseas. There is still much difficulty in obtaining an adequate supply of helpers at sowing and lifting times although mechanical contrivances like the potato-lifter work well in the level fields.

Many farmers specialise in the commercial production of raspberries. The districts of Blairgowrie and Forfar are best known but there are many other parts of Strathmore in which temperatures, soil and exposure favour their cultivation. The varieties grown are intended for jam making and for table and canning purposes. The crop is grown on a large scale and entire fields are given over to raspberry canes. In the summertime, hundreds of people, students, holiday-makers, etc., are employed in picking the fruit. The bulk of the crop is despatched in barrels to fruit merchants or jam manufacturers in Forfar, Montrose, Dundee and in England.

Another farming activity in Strathmore and indeed in the entire Angus-Perthshire-Kincardine area is the rearing and fattening of Aberdeen-Angus cattle. It was only at the start of last century that the first attempt was made, at a Strathmore farm, to improve the black, hornless cattle. But, ever since, in every part of the three counties, heavy-fleshed store cattle have been reared and beef of prime quality produced. Quality has always been the aim of the Aberdeen-Angus stock raiser and it is little wonder that pedigree bulls of well-known Strathmore herds always attract overseas buyers at the annual bull sales at Perth.

In the Howe of the Mearns, an extension of Strathmore in Kincardine, farming also is a major activity. The land is low, sheltered somewhat by the Grampian Mountains and covered by a thick mantle of bright red clay. Agriculture is less varied, however; there is no fruit growing and wheat is not of importance. Arable farming consists chiefly of oats, barley and main crop potatoes. Much land is in grass, and turnips are grown for stock-feeding. There are not many farms without herds of beef cattle, for in the Mearns stock rearing is an essential part of farm economy.

At the other end of the strath, in the lower basins of rivers Almond and Earn, farming is again of the utmost importance. Arable cropping is blended with stock rearing. The straths have easy gradients and their workable soils provide very productive farm land. But, as in the carse of the river Isla, the riverlands of Strathearn are not put to their best use because they are subject to annual flooding.

Spaced out at regular intervals throughout Strathmore are towns whose site in this farming area gives the clue to their importance. Such places as Coupar Angus (2,000), Forfar (10,000), Brechin (7,000), and Laurencekirk (1,500) are well suited to serve the needs of the farming community. They are good examples of market towns. They all stand on a railway route and each is a focal centre of roads. In Forfar, the largest town, a range of textiles and soft drinks are made. Brechin, also, has textile works and makes machine tools.

Strathmore provides an easy route for the main road and railway from Perth to Aberdeen.

The Sidlaw Hills. The Sidlaw Hills belong to the volcanic ranges which run across the Central Lowlands. Detached from the Ochil Hills by the intervention of the Tay and Earn valleys, this range runs eastwards to Dundee beyond which it decreases in height in the direction of Montrose. At their western end, the Sidlaws appear as a definite chain of hills with a steep southern slope. At Perth, for example, Kinnoull Hill presents a sheer scarp face to the carse below. But in the vicinity of Dundee, they appear as low ridges with intervening undulations. Dundee Law (571 feet) and its lower neighbour, the Balgay Hill (362 feet) are well known examples of old volcanic plugs which stand out as squat conical summits.

An abundance of hill pasture as well as an expanse of heather-clad moorland limit the mode of farming to sheep rearing on the Sidlaws. But on some of the western hills, where drainage has been undertaken, there are plantations of young conifers. In the vicinity of Dundee, where the land becomes less steep, there are substantial farmsteads and the standard of farming is high. Stock raising and crop growing are well blended, both grain and root crops being successfully cultivated up to 750 feet on the southern slopes of the hills. In these eastern hills, a few miles from the city, are situated some of the reservoirs which provide Dundee with its water supply.

The Carse of Gowrie. The Carse of Gowrie lies below the Sidlaw Hills, adjacent to the river Tay. It is a broad plain extending from Perth to Dundee. Seldom does it rise more than 100 feet above the level of the river and many parts are exceedingly flat. This carseland consists of estuarine clays and alluvial soils of great fertility. Several low eminences or 'inches' of rich dark loam appear above the plain. They existed as secure islands standing above the general level of the carselands at a time when the carse was water-logged or subject to frequent flooding.

12

The entire carse is one of the most fertile areas of Scotland. It possesses a fine combination of advantages – sunny exposure, little rainfall, level terrain, fertile soils and the protection of the Sidlaw Hills. The carseland clays are fertile but their stickiness makes their cultivation very difficult. Modern mechanical contrivances make tillage easier, yet the excellence of the carse as an arable and pastoral area is due to the perseverance and experience of the farmers themselves.

FIG. 64 The inches and lines of communication in the Carse of Gowrie (*Crown copyright reserved*)

There are very good crops of wheat which thrives on the heavy carseland. Oats are grown for seed and oat straw is used for feeding and bedding cattle. Hay is a necessity on livestock farms and beans are a favourite fodder crop. Turnips and potatoes are common, the one for cattle feeding, the other for the seed trade and for the early market. There are fields of raspberries and some apple orchards. On many farms, the heavy soils carry permanent pasture which makes good grazing for Aberdeen-Angus and Shorthorn store cattle.

The complete absence of steep gradients bestows a distinct advantage on the carseland as a corridor of communication. A modern trunk road and a direct rail service provide easy and quick routes between Perth and Dundee. Road traffic, from Dundee to Perth and beyond, is particularly well served by the fast dual carriageway that now traverses the level carseland.

The Angus-Kincardine Coastal Region. The coasts of these two counties show a rare variety of rocky beaches, precipitous cliffs and sandy stretches. From Broughty Ferry to Buddon Ness and Carnoustie, there are obvious traces of raised beaches at the 20 feet level and higher. Around Carnoustie, Lunan Bay, and Montrose, the broad sandy beaches are backed by links and dunes of spiny grasses and rough pasture. Near Arbroath, the coast is of red sandstone cliffs and sea erosion is seen most markedly in the sculpturing of arches, miniature stacks, creeks and rocky inlets. Around Stonehaven, with its beach of stone and shingle, the coast is likewise bold and rocky with sheer cliffs furrowed by caves and galleries. It is a popular bathing resort. In Angus excellent sandy beaches, ideal golf links, fine coastal scenery, plentiful summer sunshine, all account for the popularity of Montrose, Arbroath and Carnoustie as holiday resorts.

Catering for an influx of summer visitors is, however, not the sole activity of these towns. **Montrose (11,000),** situated at the road and rail bridge point of the broad tidal basin of the river Esk, has a small motor-vessel fishing fleet. Boat building, flax and jute spinning and bread flour making are carried on. Jam making, fruit and vegetable canning are also important. **Arbroath (20,000),** where in 1320 Scottish independence was asserted by the signing of the Declaration of Arbroath, is second to Dundee in population but relatively much less important in industrial activity. It has similar textile works. Textile machinery and lawn mowers are made as well as boilers and air conditioning plant. Codling and haddock are landed by its fishing fleet – Arbroath smoked fish are particularly popular. **Carnoustie (5,500)** has jam, jute and shoe factories while the production of cranes is also carried on.

All along this coastal strip there is very good farming land. Even though the tracts of links such as at Barry have long been used as military training grounds, their rough pasture provides grazing for sheep. In many parts the coastlands are very level. The soils are mixed in character but there are fertile deep loams and productive sandy terraces. Mixed farming is general. Potatoes, seed and ware,

are very popular and thrive well on the lighter, stoneless soils. Oats are grown extensively; wheat and barley are suited to the sunny and dry summers. Dairying is a common practice in the proximity of the coastal towns. But Kincardine's coast is too exposed for wheat to be a success. Oats are most common and so are potatoes and turnips. Beef cattle are more numerous than dairy herds. In the vicinity of Dundee, market gardening is carried on; tomato cultivation in glasshouses and flower nurseries are both common.

The coastal strip, of easy gradient, is utilised by the main road and rail routes from Dundee to Aberdeen.

The two main towns of this region are Dundee and Perth.

Dundee (185,200). Dundee, spread around the prominent Law Hill overlooking the Tay estuary, is the third largest city of Scotland. It derives much of its current importance from its long and unique experience of a variety of textile fibres. Its trade in linen products and yarn, still extant, has at least two centuries of tradition behind it; even at an earlier date its coarse woollens and plaidings earned recognition in Europe. Jute made its appearance in Dundee factories over a hundred years ago. Its arrival was precipitated by the cessation of imports of flax from Russia at the time of the Crimean War. But merchants were already familiar with jute, a coarse tawny fibre derived from a cane-like plant grown in the deltaic soils of the river Ganges. The versatile character of jute made it readily acceptable in industry and the manufacture of jute products brought a spectacular advancement to the textile activities of Dundee. The dependence on jute is not now so complete but Dundee remains the premier centre of jute manufacture in Great Britain. All the common sorts of bags and sacks are jute products; so are hessian (jute pieces), linoleum backing and tarpaulin. Not so familiar are its other manifold uses; carpets, upholstery strapping, stiffening in suitings, lining in footwear, cable binding, twine, and string.

Jute has enjoyed so much prominence that the other industrial aspects of the town often receive scant attention. There is light engineering in addition to bitumen and oil refining. Its paper and publishing trade includes the production of newspapers and journals and the manufacture of post cards and calendars. The manufacture of jam, marmalade and sweets contribute to the town's reputation. Its shipyards produce tankers and cargo vessels up to 30,000 tons per annum. At a more recent date, Dundee extended its industrial activities by developing an industrial estate on high ground to the north of the city. The great variety of articles produced provides diversity to the present industrial pattern of Dundee and widens the range of employment for its male and female workers. Automatic products like cash registers, electronic adding and accounting machines, fluid measuring meters and petrol pump computers are assembled. So also are domestic refrigerators and spin dryers. There are factories which produce expanded rubber, artificial teeth, electronic valves, dry batteries, industrial gloves, travel goods and vehicle components. Ladies' and children's dresses, underwear and overalls are made up and there is canning of fruit and vegetables. With such an assortment, Dundee's industrial estate exemplifies the rapid growth of new industry in the city in post-war years.

But a town seldom fulfils one function only. Dundee is not merely an industrial city. The location of the town assures its importance as a centre of communications. The pattern of its communications differs from that of Perth in a striking manner. On the north side of the river and along the Angus coasts easy gradients enable several road and rail routes to converge on the city. Now, in addition to the famous Tay bridge (completed 1888), there is a new road bridge providing an important link between Dundee and the south through Fife. (See Fig. 60, pp 155).

Dundee is one of the larger east coast ports. Its docks have witnessed busier times and more direct exchange with European lands. Its import trade is now restricted to essential commodities. Jute is the major import but cargoes of tea, grain, timber, pulp, and unrefined sugar are discharged. Its export trade, meagre in comparison, consists of general cargo like manufactured jute products, seed potatoes, linoleum and machinery. But, like many other manufacturing towns, many of its products go to Glasgow for transhipment overseas. Queen's College (now to be a University independent of St. Andrews) and the art, commercial, and technical institutions make Dundee an important centre of education.

Perth (41,000). Throughout the long history of Perth, geographical position has always been an important factor. As a capital of Scotland and a seat of government, the town possessed locational advantages superior to Edinburgh, its successor. As a port at the head of navigation, it conducted an extensive trade with north European countries prior to its eclipse by the industrial growth of

Dundee. Perth lies between the Ochil and Sidlaw Hills in the gap breached by the river Tay. Here, by the level inches flanking the river, there was a bridge across the river, six centuries ago. Perth still retains the function of a bridge town. A railway bridge as well as two road bridges span the river, (only now is there another road bridge over the Tay below Perth). Roads and railways, for the most part following the less resistant gradients, converge on Perth from every direction. (See fig. 57, p. 145.) It is, therefore, of much importance as a centre of communication.

Such transport facilities make it well suited to be a convenient market centre, especially since the entire neighbourhood is predominantly agricultural. Perth bull sales are universally known; its auction marts handle great numbers of livestock. Perth is the centre of disposal of farm products and for the supply of equipment, seeds, etc.

The industries of Perth and its manufactures cover a wide range. The town has earned a great reputation as a centre for cleaning and dyeing, especially dry cleaning and the manufacture of machinery for this industry. In addition to its creamery, there are printing, carpet and tailoring pursuits. Whisky is blended and bottled in the town and at a new plant at Inveralmond. Its glass industry is of great importance because of the variety of products made – laboratory, heavy chemical, and toughened engineering glassware. As a centre for tourists, too, Perth has the distinct advantage of being within easy distance of an abundance of fine highland scenery and there is excellent fishing in the river Tay.

XV · THE SOUTHERN UPLANDS

THE Southern Uplands lie to the south of the Central Lowlands. They contain great stretches of moorland both in the east and west but in physical appearance, in contrast to the Highlands, the land is not so high and is less rugged. As in the Highlands, however, there is a distinct contrast between the wetter western zone and the eastern parts where sunshine of greater duration is accompanied by a very low rainfall.

In contrast to the Central Lowlands, there is a scarcity of coal measures and thus it is that, except in the mid-Tweed valley, the development of industry has not assumed the pattern or the magnitude of production of the Central Lowlands. The density of population is nowhere very high. The urban population is restricted to a number of small market and textile towns. For the most part, the region is rural and there is a country population grouped in small villages or scattered in hill, dale, and lowland farming units.

This region lies astride the lines of communication which link England with Central Scotland. Except that the busy Glasgow–Carlisle route, via the Clyde and Annan valleys, must surmount the steep ascent of Beattock Summit (1,000 feet high), the Southern Uplands are more easy to negotiate than the Highlands. The main routes which traverse this southern part of Scotland take full advantage of the lines of least physical resistance along which road and rail traffic is very heavy.

Galloway and Dumfriesshire. Galloway (the counties of Wigtown and Kirkcudbright) and Dumfriesshire occupy the entire south-west corner of Scotland. In general, the land is highest along the Ayrshire border and lowest along the Solway Firth. The region has four different physical characteristics:

(a) The high moors of resistant granite in the north, wild in aspect, bare and remote. There is the Kells Range of Kirkcudbright and a cluster of summits above 2,000 feet, with Merrick (2,764) highest of all.

(b) The coastal lowlands bordering the Solway Firth, covered by glacial deposits and good quality soils. To the west, the Rhinns and Machers of Wigtown, well marked by drumlins, extend as low flats far out into the firth with Luce Bay and Loch Ryan separated by a narrow neck of level land. Eastwards, the coastlands consist of rugged hills with Criffell rising as an imposing granite mass to 1,866 feet. In Dumfriesshire, low and undulating land stretches along the narrowing firth to the border with England.

(c) The dales of the rivers which flow southwards in parallel courses to the firth. The Nith and Annan dales are the most important for their valleys are more open. The river Dee, draining a large

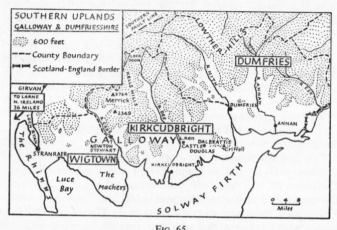

FIG. 65

area of the Galloway highlands, has the long and narrow Loch Ken as part of its course.

(d) The Solway Firth, triangular in shape, tapers to an apex at the English-Scottish border. Its tides are very rapid and treacherous, the incoming flow sweeping in like a race. At low water, a monotonous expanse of sand stretches along the coast.

In this region agriculture is of paramount importance. The great expanse of uplands as well as the extension of lowlands in the Rhinns and Machers of Wigtown account as much for farming activities as do the mild temperatures and copious rainfall. Economic as well as geographical influences explain the high productivity of livestock reached by the experienced farming community. A rich and expanding market is assured in the urban centres of central Scotland and northern England.

The very important dairying industry is now long enough established to be well organised both for maximum production and efficient marketing of milk. The cow population is commonly of the Ayrshire breed. The output of milk in the south-west of Scotland increased by 25 per cent in the ten years ending 1962. Grass and turnips are customary fodder crops and the practice of drying grass is increasing. Dairy farms, connected to an electrical supply derived from the Galloway hydro-electric stations, make common use of electrical equipment and local creameries deal with the preparation of milk products like fresh and tinned milk, cheese and butter. Dairying is widespread in the coastal lowlands and in the dales.

The rough grazings of the uplands carry both sheep and cattle. In the more exposed parts of Galloway, Blackface sheep predominate but elsewhere Cheviot and Crossbreed animals are found. On hill farms and in some of the dales, the fattening of beef cattle is common. 'Galloways', all black or in the attractive 'belted' coat, are robust and yield beef of good quality. Outwintering is common with hay and turnips as extra feed.

Arable farming, of secondary importance to livestock and grass, is a feature of the Solway farms. The most common cereal is oats and there is a little wheat. Potatoes are most popular; in Wigtown, it is mild enough for 'earlies' but in the other counties the main crop is lifted in the autumn.

Within recent years, a large amount of moorland, hillside and valley has been planted in young forests, mainly of the coniferous types. They are found in every part of this region. The best known is the Glen Trool National Forest, the second largest in Scotland. Here, among magnificent mountain and loch scenery, has been established a camping site used more and more by holiday-makers every year. The National Forest covers over 100,000 acres and consists of five forest areas. Forestry provides employment for several hundred workers. They live in or near the country towns or in the forestry villages constructed specially to provide homes for forest workers and their families. Minnoch village, north of Newton Stewart, contains workers on the Glen Trool forests and the village of Ae, not far north of Dumfries, is a similar forestry community begun in 1947.

Fishing, also, provides a livelihood for local people and a form of recreation for sportsmen and visitors. There is plenty of loch and river fishing. The rivers Nith, Annan, and Cree are well noted for good salmon and trout fishing. The Solway Firth has always had a reputation for its fisheries. Salmon, trout and codling are usually obtained by small craft and stake nets are in use along the sandy flats.

Dumfries (27,000) is the largest and most important town of south-west Scotland. It has outgrown its early site which was on a copse-covered mound, at a crossing point on a bend of the river Nith. The development of the railway system to the town in the middle of last century enhanced its function as a market centre rather than as a port. The rural character of the county is, in large part, reflected in its urban activities. The town is a regular and convenient place for the sale of livestock and the purchase of agricultural equipment, seeds, and fertilisers. It has grain mills which handle the local crops; it manufactures feeding stuffs; it despatches seed potatoes and tinned milk is prepared. The textile industry of Dumfries, still using some local wool, embraces a variety of knitted garments for home and foreign markets. Engineering has now taken the place of a former coach and motor car industry. The manufacture of rubber footwear is another activity and there is now a plastics plant for making polyester film. Dumfries is an administrative centre and it is a focus of rail, and even more so, of road communications from three directions.

Annan (5,000) is a little town situated on the left bank of the river of the same name. It is a town of great age, having been created a royal burgh in 1538. It is no longer important as a port but salmon fishing and shrimp catching give work to a number of its townsfolk. The agricultural neighbourhood accounts for its importance as a market centre; oat milling and animal food preparation are carried on. Its engineering works is well known for the great number and variety of boilers which it produces but cranes and machinery are also made in the town. There is a chip-board factory and, at Chapelcross, near the town, is situated Scotland's first plutonium and nuclear generating station, now with four reactors, operated by the Atomic Energy Authority. Such a modern development provides employment for process and scientific workers and adds to the repute of the town.

In Galloway, there are few towns and none are very large in size or in population. They are quiet rural centres with fine woodland and river scenery at hand. Most of them have weekly livestock markets but some are noted for particular activities. Dalbeattie (3,000) has a creamery and a textile factory and there are granite quarries nearby. Four miles away is Castle Douglas (3,000), a noted fishing centre. Kirkcudbright (2,500), on the river Dee, has milk and textile factories; it is near the Tongland power station of the Galloway hydro-electric scheme. Newton Stewart (2,000), on the river Cree, manufactures pre-cast products, woollen rugs and scarves; it is also a fishing resort. For such rural centres, road communications (car, bus, farm vehicle) are now of supreme importance.

Stranraer (9,000) is important in two respects. It is the commercial, administrative and agricultural centre of Wigtownshire, dealing with dairy produce and farm requirements, as well as making children's clothing. As the town lies at the inner end of sheltered Loch Ryan, it has a distinct advantage as the port for the daily steamer service to Larne. This route, stormy at times, is much in favour for passenger, mail, and freight traffic because the open sea passage across the North Channel is only 36 miles in length. From Northern Ireland, come regular supplies of fish, mushrooms, eggs, poultry and milk. The channel boats provide a ferry service convenient for hundreds of holiday makers and their cars.

The Tweed Basin. The Tweed basin embraces the entire southeast corner of Scotland. In general, the land is at its highest in the uplands around the basin. The lowest part is in the riverlands of the Merse. The region has four different physical characteristics:

(a) The upland rim. In the north, the Moorfoot and Lammermuir Hills extend in a broad arc of rounded ranges and open moors with grassy slopes. In the west, throughout Tweeddale, there are clusters of hill ranges with many summits like Dollar Law, Broad Law and Hart Fell, all nearly 3,000 feet. In the south, the Cheviot Hills stretch across the greater part of the border and form a distinct upland zone of hard rock, highest in the granite block of The Cheviot (2,676 feet). The hills are dome shaped, open and desolate, with tracts of rough pasture and peat bog.

(b) The dales. The upland rim is furrowed by the steep valleys of numerous hill burns which join the larger tributaries and they in turn drain into the main river. The Tweed, itself, curves northwards and eastwards through a dale of singular beauty. At Peebles, where the Tweed has completed one-third of its course, it has dropped

1,000 feet from its source which is near the Annan and Clyde head-waters. Left bank tributaries like the Gala and Leader Waters descend through dales with narrow haughs. The slopes of the right bank tributaries, Yarrow, Ettrick, and Teviot are steep but their valleys open out into wider haughlands.

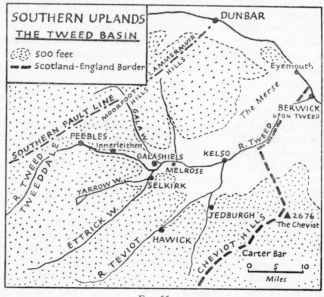

FIG. 66

(c) The plain of the Tweed. From Peebles eastwards, the river Tweed is contained by steep slopes. Below Galashiels, as it winds and turns on its way to the North Sea at Berwick-upon-Tweed, the river flows through the Merse. The Merse is a broad and level river plain of deep loam and clay broken in places by undulating terrain.

(d) The Berwickshire coast. Save for the accessible bays and sandy stretches at Eyemouth and Coldingham, the Berwickshire coast is rocky with high picturesque red cliffs.

In climate the broad differences between west and east and between upland and lowland prevail. The heavy rainfall of the hill groups of the Upper Tweed contrast with the lighter fall in the middle reaches and with the extreme eastern lowlands where the annual amount is less than 30 inches. Everywhere on the upland stretches, altitude makes for a lowering of temperatures; on the lowlands the western parts of Galloway have a milder winter than the seaward parts of the Merse. In summer, though it is warm throughout the Solway area, there is greater assurance of summer sunshine in the Merse and coastal strip of Berwickshire.

The entire basin, one of the richest agricultural belts of Scotland, is extremely well used. In pastoral as in arable pursuits, the farmers of south-east Scotland have, for almost two centuries, passed on a legacy of experience both in the management of their soil and in the rearing of their stock. On the extensive moorland, high above the river Tweed, roam great numbers of sheep. In the counties of Roxburgh, Peebles, Selkirk, and Berwick, the concentration of sheep is at its greatest in the whole of Scotland. There is ample grazing ground, clothed in rough grass and heather on which no other stock can thrive successfully for a very long time. The Black-face flocks predominate on the higher pastures. Their hardiness befits the rigours of the climate at such altitudes yet seldom is there a winter when shepherds are not obliged, at some time, to rescue stranded sheep and sustain them with hay when snow is on the ground. Cheviots and Crossbreeds are popular at lower levels, in the dales and even in the more arable lands of the basin. Along the river haughs and in the dales much land is under cultivation and there is also grazing for cattle. The Merse is the most fertile part of the basin. The level land and the fertile soil are well suited to a great variety of crops. Barley is the most important but there are fine yields of wheat and oats. Potatoes are common but turnips and hay, both essential for stock-feeding, cover a great acreage. Sugar beet is produced, while good quality beef cattle and dairy herds are kept on many farms.

In one respect the Tweed basin is unique. There are no local coal measures and, so far, there has been no development of hydro-electricity. Yet industrial activities have been successfully pursued and it is in the group of small textile towns in the middle part of the basin that the density of population of the Southern Uplands is at its greatest.

There appear to be traces of the existence of a domestic weaving industry in the area, sponsored, at an early date, by monks skilled in sheep husbandry. But the most positive impetus to the textile industry was the mechanisation of the Industrial Revolution. The very first and essential requisite for the driving of machinery – an abundance of water – was at hand and mills rapidly appeared along the banks of the river Tweed and of its principal tributaries. The supplies of wool came at first directly from the sheep grazed in the district.

FIG. 67 The sites of Galashiels and Selkirk

Steam and electric plant have now replaced water-power and coal has to be brought from the Central Lowlands. The abundance of water, soft in character, is still an important asset in the processing of wool. Such is the great variety and high quality of the woollen manufactures that local supplies of wool are no longer sufficient or suitable. The Border wool trade imports wool principally from the Commonwealth but also from other sheep grazing lands and some of the raw materials consist of natural fibres of animals other than the sheep.

The chief centres of manufacture are Peebles, Innerleithen, Galashiels, Selkirk, Hawick, and Jedburgh. As in the north of England, the textile factories employ a large number of women workers. But there the similarity ends. Both the Tweed towns and their factories are relatively small. There is not the heavy concentration of industry nor the objectionable smoke-drenched atmosphere.

Galashiels (12,000), at the mouth of the Gala Water, is a major textile centre. Although it was early identified with weaving, the town was a product of the eighteenth century when its mills made cloth, blankets and shawls, all in coloured designs. Such a background helps to account for the inherited skill now evident in its tweed, blankets, rugs, tartans, yarns and high class knitwear. Its products are of world wide repute. The Technical College promotes study and research in the woollen industry. It is important, too, for textile machinery and electronic circuit printing. Selkirk (6,000) and Peebles (5,000) also have mills making suitings, cloths and scarves from the finest of wools.

Hawick (17,000), the other important centre, is situated at the crook or confluence of the river Teviot and the Slitrig Water. The arrangement of the town and its factories conforms very much to the courses of these rivers. The supply of water has been and still is an important factor in its industrial activities. After a stormy history, the town emerged as a textile centre in the second half of the eighteenth century, a period which marked the start of its prosperity and extension. Carpet making (started in 1752) preceded the manufacture of stockings and the practice of frame knitting. But the requirements of current fashion have evoked many changes and developments in Hawick's knitwear trade, attended at every stage by an increase in technical skill, experience and improvements in the use of mechanical contrivances. The town is an important centre for the manufacture of underwear and of very high grade woollen garments, particularly women's jumpers, cardigans, twin-sets and sweaters, each varied in style as in colour range. Far removed though Hawick and the Himalayas are, their association cannot be closer for it is not so much local wool as cashmere fibres from the highland goat of Central Asia along with fine Australian merino wool that keep the frames of its mills occupied all the year round. The demand for its knitwear garments is world wide but the best in quality and most up-to-date in fashion finds a consistent market in America, even in the face of locally produced garments.

The Border country has much to delight the visitor – the woodland and river scenery around Peebles; the superb view from the Eildons above Melrose (2,000); the wealth of historic lore of abbeys like Melrose and Dryburgh; the literary associations of the Scott country around Abbotsford and the famous salmon fishing on the Tweed. On such attributes has the reputation of the Borders as a tourist area been founded. Modern road and rail transport make it easily accessible. The main east coast railway and trunk road (A1) go through Berwick and the 'Waverley' rail route passes through Hawick and Galashiels. The high road over the Cheviots via Carter Bar also leads from England down into the valley while roads run east to west along the riverlands. Most Border towns are thus route centres and crossing points as well as being market and shopping centres. For the visitor there is good hotel and hostel accommodation.

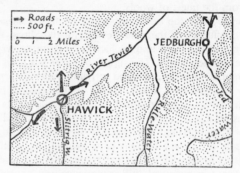

FIG. 68 The sites of Hawick and Jedburgh

In the district around Peebles, several forests of the Forestry Commission such as Glentress provide employment locally while Eyemouth (2,000) is a small fishing port and resort. Berwick-upon-Tweed (13,000), the main town in the Merse, is an ancient Border town which has been part of England since 1482. It is noted for salmon fisheries but it is not a port of importance. Its three bridges (an old and a new road bridge and a railway bridge and viaduct) make Berwick an important crossing point between Scotland and England.

XVI · THE HIGHLAND ZONE*

THE HIGHLANDS AND ISLANDS

THE Highlands of Scotland form one of the most distinct regions in Great Britain, and the 'frontier' of the north boundary fault is physically stronger, and more complete, than that between England and Scotland. The physical demarcation of this region, which is so clear on the map and on the ground, is matched by a less complete, but a very significant boundary between the Lowland and Highland ways of life. For both physical background and the present human activities, we must draw our line not merely at the north boundary fault, but along the eastern margins of the Highlands also, and then consider the east coast lowlands (and Orkney) as a separate region. These lowlands share little with the major area of mountain, moorland and glen, except northerly latitude, and some of its climatic and economic effects (such as cool summers and lengthy lines of communication).

The distinctive environment and characteristic cultural pattern have been interwoven in a long process of historical development, and in this there has been some continuity with the north-east lowlands, and some discontinuity within the Highlands and Islands. The streams of Celtic and Norse migrations mingled in the island and coastal fringes of Scotland, the former most strongly influencing the south and west, the latter the north and east. The more vigorous Norsemen took in the Hebrides, as well as the Northern Isles, however, and held them until the thirteenth century. Not until two centuries later was the whole Highland Zone politically integrated with Scotland, and the period of allegiance to the Lordship of the Isles increased the tradition of separate regional unity in the Highlands.

Turning to the geographical facts of today, we find a relatively

*The term 'Highland Zone' is used in this chapter to refer to that area of Scotland named 'Northern Highlands' in the earlier description of Scotland's physical geography. This change of name for the whole of the region north of the fault line should emphasise the idea that it contains more than the single feature referred to – the Highlands – and is in fact a whole zone of environment and activity.

stable pattern of land-use, with four main elements: (i) the mountains
and moorland used for maintaining deer and grouse – large estates
owned or rented for sport, but with some rough grazing for sheep

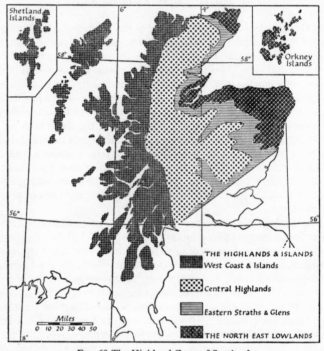

FIG. 69 The Highland Zone of Scotland

and cattle; (ii) the hill sheep farms; (iii) the forests; (iv) the crofters'
holdings. The first and second of these require and support only a
very small and scattered population: not many shepherds and game-
keepers are needed to care for wide areas. Forestry gives rise to an
occasional new village, and reinforces here and there the existing
rural settlements. The strongest single element in the human geography of this region is, however, one with a very distinctive way of
life – crofting, and the main settlement pattern is that of the crofting
township.

Crofts are small holdings derived from the division of farmland in the eighteenth and nineteenth centuries, and they generally share the use of common pastures. The word 'croft' originally referred to the arable land which had been reclaimed in the valleys and along the coast. Often peat had to be removed and seaweed applied as manure, and this process of re-clamation by 'skinning' is still pursued in some areas. As popu-lation grew in the later eighteenth and early nineteenth centuries, and as the clearances from the inland glens of the mainland in-creased the demands on coastal land, cultivation extended into the poorer land of the moorland edge, but the demarcation be-tween crops and rough grazing has fluctuated, and in this century of depopulation the moorland has returned to many areas.

FIG. 70 The deer forests of Scotland (see also fig. 81)

While lack of arable land precludes the larger rural unit of settle-ment – the village – the need for co-operation in the activities of the croft has favoured the compact townships of two or more farm-teams. The main reason for the grouping of crofter families in teams was, at one time, the joint ownership of the land, but since the early nineteenth century this system of tenure has gone, and it is the work of harvesting, cutting and carrying peat, fishing, and even building, that still calls for mutual effort. The township has preserved, how-ever, its function of communal tenure in the open grazings which are shared by the crofters on the moor or the machair – the level, sandy, shoreland. (The sheep and cattle on the common grazing are tended by a village herd or buachaille.) Thus we find croft-land for arable and permanent pasture, and common grazing where each crofter has the right to pasture a number of animals (his souming). The individual croft has usually less than nine acres, and often less than five acres, of croft-land.

The crofting population forms rather less than half of the popu-lation of the seven 'crofting counties', namely Argyll, Caithness, Inverness, Orkney, Ross and Cromarty, Sutherland and Shetland.

The townships vary in size from five to fifty crofts, usually fifteen to twenty, and are typically situated in more favoured coastal and valley areas, marginal to the major mountain blocks. The haughland in the valleys, and the raised beaches along the coast are more suitable for cultivation, both in providing flatter land and deeper soils. The presence of blown shell-sand along the coast is an additional asset, especially if good drainage reduces soil acidity and so enables the crofter to improve his land more readily. Townships

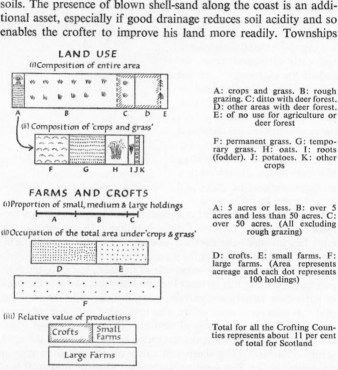

LAND USE
(i) Composition of entire area

A: crops and grass. B: rough grazing. C: ditto with deer forest. D: other areas with deer forest. E: of no use for agriculture or deer forest

(ii) Composition of 'crops and grass'

F: permanent grass. G: temporary grass. H: oats. I: roots (fodder). J: potatoes. K: other crops

FARMS AND CROFTS
(i) Proportion of small, medium & large holdings

A: 5 acres or less. B: over 5 acres and less than 50 acres. C: over 50 acres. (All excluding rough grazing)

(ii) Occupation of the total area under 'crops & grass'

D: crofts. E: small farms. F: large farms. (Area represents acreage and each dot represents 100 holdings)

(iii) Relative value of productions

Total for all the Crofting Counties represents about 11 per cent of total for Scotland

FIG. 71 The Economy of the Crofting Counties (see also fig 81)

may often be seen on the islands as a line of houses half way up the slope from the sea, with separate strips of arable below and rough grazing above. In the mainland valleys the crofts are more commonly scattered on the lower arable land, and where there is a coastal plain there may be no village centre at all, every house standing 100 or 200 yards from the next. Where fishing is important, fewer and smaller crofts may be very dispersed along the coast, or with only garden-size holdings there may be a compact coastal village.

Some crofts are fenced off from each other, but in other townships all are fenced in together, and then if cattle are grazed before the harvest is over they must be tethered to their owners' strips. But the rough grazing is always open, and each crofter has the right to graze a certain number of animals there. The main limitation in the keeping of cattle is the shortage of winter feeding stuffs; in rearing sheep it is the quality of pastures.

In the past the crofter lived more completely on his own resources: corn for oatmeal, potatoes, dairy produce, eggs, and meat all came from the croft. (It was always necessary to buy some corn from the Lowlands and to pay for this by the sale of cattle.) For those who lived near coast and loch, fish were an important supplement, and could be cheaply bought in other townships, and salted herring lasted through the winter months. From the moorland and the sheep came peat and wool, providing fuel and clothing – at the cost of much labour for the whole family. There was a complete sequence of seasonal activities, and a full use of traditional skills and customs. The pressure of work varied with the season, and after the harvest (and perhaps herring fishing later on) the winter was a time of comparative ease – especially for the men.

The decay of this way of life was most rapid and thorough where the clearances were most severe, but in this century the whole of the region has suffered depopulation and has become more dependent on the lowlands for goods and services. Today the croft is rarely more than a part-time holding, and many occupations such as forestry work and catering for tourists, supplement the earnings from the sale of produce from the croft. The average croft now consumes rather less than half its own produce, so that adequate communications are necessary for both marketing produce and purchasing supplies. While in some crofts oil-lamps and peat fires remain, electricity has lightened the labour in many townships, and the crofter may now have his car and tractor. Much that was distinct in the culture of the region has weakened, yet, while the crofter remains attached to his croft, the old and the new elements in his environment can be blended, and some of his unique traditions can persist. Despite the hardships, there is a strong attraction still in the freedom and independence which the secure tenure of a croft ensures: it rarely provides a living, but it is a guarantee against complete destitution; it is a refuge against times of unemployment and old age.

The stability of the crofters' holdings is the key to the continuity of settlement which is vital in the sparsely populated Highlands. Though many holdings are no longer occupied, and many have been

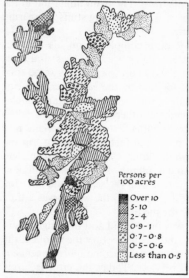

Persons per
100 acres

Over 10
5 - 10
2 - 4
0·9 - 1
0·7 - 0·8
0·5 - 0·6
Less than 0·5

FIG. 72 Density of population of West Highlands (1951)

merged, the distribution is essentially that of 1886, when crofters were at last secure from eviction. This post-clearance pattern is a remnant of what had once existed. The severe limits set by physical conditions largely account for the fact that the seven crofting counties, covering nearly half Scotland's area, contain little more than one-twentieth of the population. Only fifty years ago, however, this fraction was half as large again, and two centuries ago the whole Highland region (about three-quarters of Scotland's area) is estimated to have maintained about a quarter of her population.

The region as a whole must therefore be seen as one of changing value in the nation's economy, for, despite over-population in the nineteenth century, the movement of people from the region has been matched by a neglect of those resources which do exist. The wider pre-clearance distribution was based on a system of land-use in which cattle – if only of a poor type by modern standards – were more important than sheep; and in many areas the summer shieling gave more extensive grazing. (The shieling was a small hut to which the young folk would move with the cattle in summer, situated on higher or more distant pastures.) The glens where men made room for sheep were overgrazed for many years until the pastures degenerated and were leased as sporting estates.

As in the study of Scotland as a whole, one can distinguish in the Highlands variations of conditions from north to south, and from east to west. The county divisions are into east-west areas, extending from the mainland to the islands, and this is especially marked in the narrower North-west Highlands. The counties south of Glen More are more radially distributed around the hub of the Grampians. These county divisions are, in part, a practical regionalism of administration, based on access from lowland areas. They had greater validity as geographical units in the past. Accessibility decreases from south to north as well as from east to west, and air travel in particular has changed the pattern of communications to one oriented on the Central Lowlands rather than on the east coast plains.

Geographically the division can best be made in north to south alignment, for the mountains separate the seaward western coast and islands from the landward straths and glens which open to the eastern plains. There are then three regions to study: (1) the West Coast and Islands; (2) the Central Highlands; (3) the Eastern Straths and Glens.

I. THE WEST COAST AND ISLANDS

Here, remoteness and exposure to the Atlantic Ocean provide common elements in a diverse, and much fragmented, region. The coastal lowlands are narrow and few roads can be made around the succession of sea-lochs which break up the coastline. The most detached peninsulas may be, in fact, as isolated as the islands. Life has been centred on the coastal sites for three reasons: the advantage of flat raised-beach, or loch-head slopes (with better drainage, and sometimes with machair land); the fishing of the Minch and other inshore waters; and the communications by sea which make life more than a primitive subsistence. But it is unfortunate that so much of the flat land is in the Outer Hebrides, where the problem of communications is most difficult. It is the Outer Hebrides, in fact, which form the 'missing' coastal plain of the Western Highlands, and the valleys of the mainland suffer from the detachment of a north to south lowland, almost as much as the Islands themselves. That many of the peninsulas of the mainland are as isolated as the Islands is reflected in the relatively high loss of population from their townships within recent years.

Climatically, this region has the advantage of more direct winter warmth from the Atlantic, and lower rainfall than the mountainous interior, but exposure to strong winds is a factor which limits both agriculture and settlement, and the rainfall varies very greatly over this narrow coastal belt and island fringe. Protection from wind; lower rainfall; better soil; a good harbour: these or other inducements are needed for the survival of population today, as once they were needed to attract the first settlers. Nevertheless, in this region more than in any other, local advantages are of little use economically without good communications, and even where these exist high transport costs affect the purchase and sale of every article of trade, and cripple many enterprises and developments which would otherwise flourish.

The Islands

It is not possible to consider all the islands in detail, but some generalisations and examples will help to explain both the unity and diversity of this region. Of the total crofting population (about 140,000), nearly two-thirds live on the islands, forming a last outpost of peasant life on the fringe of industrial Britain. While depopulation continues to threaten this region, both Lewis and Shetland are overpopulated, if judged by their available wealth. The population of Lewis is still 29 per cent of that for the whole of Ross-shire.* It did not suffer from clearances on any large scale, nor was emigration as considerable as elsewhere, for the fishing industry was a strong source of wealth. The balance throughout the islands between a life of deprivation and one of comparative prosperity rests in the provision of work to supplement or replace the crofter's subsistence.

The decline of fishing and the absence of forestry in most of the islands leaves only a few primary resources to be utilised. Minerals are exploited in some localities, despite difficulties of transport. In north-east Skye diatomite is excavated, and even in the remote Shetland Isles minerals such as chrome ore, talc and serpentine have been worked.

*Between 1951 and 1961 Lewis lost 11 per cent of its population while Ross and Cromarty as a whole lost only 5 per cent.

Two other resources – peat and seaweed – have been domestic sources of fuel and fertility for many crofters, and both have their possibilities for modern industry. Peat has, as yet, little industrial importance but there are now three seaweed factories in operation in the Outer Hebrides. Collecting and drying, in the Uists and Lewis, precede milling in these factories to give the raw material for alginate (used in food and other products). But where soil, minerals and other material assets may be lacking, the very barrenness of the land may be of value, when combined with special beauty or tempting hazard, in attracting the tourist. At least in Skye it is the Cuillin Hills, the least productive area, which have a special appeal for the climber and naturalist. But for the holiday-maker, as for the trader, communications are vital, and only the nearer islands have the opportunity to rival the mainland coast in catering for him.

The Hebrides. The Hebrides extend for some 200 miles from south of Islay to the Butt of Lewis, and of the many islands which make up this broken archipelago, eighty were inhabited (1951). Many of these are small rocky islands and lighthouses with very few inhabitants, as the following table shows:

Number of Islands	Population Range	Total Population (1951)
35	under 10 ⎫	
24	10-200 ⎬	3,482
8	201-300 ⎭	
3	301-600	1,255
10	over 900	49,649

The ten most populous island areas* in 1961, and their increase or decrease of population between 1951 and 1961 are as follows:

Lewis	16,700	*loss*	2,077	North Uist	1,921	*loss*	300
Skye	7,765	*loss*	867	Mull	1,674	*loss*	287
South Uist	3,983	*gain*	219†	Barra	1,467	*loss*	417
Islay	3,866	*loss*	404	Tiree & Coll	1,143	*loss*	286
Harris	3,285	*loss*	706				

*Based on county districts. †The result of military installations

A greater density of population is to be found in some of the more isolated islands — Barra, Lewis, Tiree — and this would, at first, appear surprising. The explanation is not entirely to be found in the physical conditions, nor entirely in historical developments. For example, while only very small areas in the more densely populated islands rise above 200 feet, this can also be said for North Uist, Benbecula or Coll, where the population is more sparse; and, if remoteness of these islands is considered as a protection against the historical processes of depopulation, Tiree may be quoted: this island suffered little in the earlier Highland depopulation, but has lost more than half its people in the last seventy years.

The Outer Hebrides. These form a more continuous and clearly visualised region than the Inner Hebrides. They have, in general, a denser population than the average for the Highlands and Islands, and this calls for special comment. Despite the hundreds of fresh-water lochs, and the deep peat of the moorland, two factors of fertility are found. One is the natural grassland of the machair, which is found up to two miles in width behind the dunes of the west coast. Where seaweed has been added, this natural grassland has provided the islanders with arable land. Though not continuous along this coast, and much less marked in Lewis and Harris, it is of great value in the islands to the south, and particularly in North Uist. (Sand blown from the seashore and the machair benefits the soils further inland also.) The other factor of fertility is less widely found and less easily utilised: it is the boulder clay revealed beneath many areas where peat has been removed for fuel over long periods. The north-west and east sides of Lewis benefit most from this 'skinned' land, but much labour is required in working in seaweed and shell sand, and in removing boulders, if arable land is to be created, so that generally it only provides rough grazing: a poor compensation for the island's lack of machair.

The crofts of Lewis lie along the seaboard, for the interior has a forbidding extent of moor and bog; and, although it is the largest 'island' in the Hebrides, with the largest population, it is a land which has almost always known great hardship. The coastal croftland has been won from machair in parts, but more from the peat areas. The peat has been stripped to allow the subsoil and upper turf to be worked together into an adequate tilth, and in some places lazy beds have been raised. The latter are small strips of a few square yards, separated by wide ditches, and they are built up to give sufficient depth for cultivation and drainage where the soil would otherwise be too thin. But the better situated crofts have flat stretches which can be ploughed by tractors, and are artificially drained by pipes or ditches. The grazing land surrounding the crofts is usually of poor quality, and, as in Shetland, could be greatly improved by lime, fertiliser and seed, so that more stock could be reared. Partly because of poor quality grazing, the use of shielings persisted longer in Lewis than in most areas. The land is flatter, less water-ridden, and the rainfall lower in the north-west of the island, and together with the advantages of the better drained raised beaches, there are

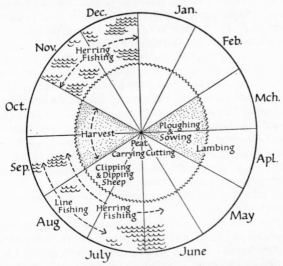

FIG. 73 Traditional work of a croft in Lewis. No such single pattern would be representative today, and many crofters now leave cultivation in other hands while working in Stornoway or beyond the Hebrides.

shell-sand and seaweed for increasing the fertility of the crofts, and so we have a denser distribution of crofting communities here.

But, like the Shetlanders, the people of Lewis have been known as fishermen, rather than crofters, and the coastal townships have taken full advantage of the inshore fishing grounds. Cod were once caught and cured for home consumption, but, during the nineteenth century, herring fishing became much more important as an industry supplying a wide market abroad, and this gave the port of Stornoway a more influential position in the island's economy. In this century the market for herring has declined, and the mainland ports have had an increasing share in the remaining landings. Stornoway (5,000) has several quays able to take ships up to 2,000 tons, but it has lost much of its trade to the mainland port of Ullapool, where there are better transport facilities.

Complementary to employment in fishing is that in the Merchant Navy, which takes many young men from the crofts for a period of years, but ensures a steady return in wages. Seasonal voyages on whaling boats are a source of further income for some Lewismen.

An industry which rose and fell in the late eighteenth and early nineteenth centuries was the burning of seaweed (kelp making). It provided a raw material for the soap and glass industries, and when this was replaced by imported supplies, a meagre, but very necessary source of income was lost. Today the manufacture of tweed has done most to compensate for the decline in fishing. Again, Stornoway plays a special part in the life of the island, for here the wool is spun and then supplied to the weavers throughout this part of the Hebrides. Although the industry has only grown up in this century, almost a thousand looms are to be found in the island today. The tendency, as in other Highland and Island communities, is for an economy to grow up based more on money earning than on cultivation of crofts, and for the larger centres like Stornoway to attract rural population.

In Lewis both fishing and textiles augment the crofters' work on the land, but in each of two areas of the Outer Hebrides where the population has not fallen so severely as elsewhere, only one of these industries is important: in Barra, fishing; in Harris, weaving. Harris contrasts with the rest of the Outer Hebrides in its broken, mountainous relief, and the population is almost entirely coastal. Only 1 per cent of the land is cultivated, and the crofts are smaller than usual, making the maximum use of the lazy beds to which creels of seaweed are brought from the beaches. While weaving is still a handloom industry in the crofts of Harris, other processes are carried out in Stornoway and Tarbert mills. It is usual to use weft spun by the crofter's wife, and warp spun in the mills; the crofter himself weaving the yarn. Fishing is of comparatively little importance, but lobsters are caught almost throughout the year, and there is some white fishing in winter and spring.

In the southern islands, there is a marked contrast between the Uists, with their dependence on crofting, and Barra where the prominence of herring fishing has already been noted. But throughout this area cattle are relatively important, and pastures have not suffered so much from over-stocking with sheep.

Although centres such as Lochboisdale and Lochmaddy have some status as centres for external and 'official' purposes, they are not focal points of island life, which is based essentially on a dispersed and little-integrated economy.

The Inner Hebrides. Mull and Skye are the two largest areas of Great Britain in which plateaux of basic lava – comparable to that of Northern Ireland – are the major structural feature. The less fluid nature of some of the outflows of lava accounts for the rugged, mountainous nature of these islands, and, although some of the smaller isles such as Rhum and Eigg share this volcanic origin, there is a general contrast between Mull and Skye on the one hand and the lower, flatter islands of Tiree and Islay, and all but Harris in the Outer Hebrides on the other.

Skye shows that broken outline of peninsula and loch which is found on the mainland coast, and suffers the same difficulties of communications. Here too, as in Harris, the population (about three-quarters living on the crofts), has a markedly coastal distribution, avoiding the bare and mountainous interior. There is no considerable fishing industry, although small boats use Portree harbour, and there is some lobster fishing around the island's coasts. Textiles are of little significance in the economy of Skye, and it is a land of small farms and crofts, with very varied degrees of prosperity. Much depends on the pastures of the more fertile northern area, and there is little arable land except in favoured stretches of raised beach and glacial drift. Subsidiary occupations for the crofter are often found in catering for tourists, and in public services such as road work. The sea makes its contribution to many homes through the merchant seamen whose wives maintain the crofts while they are away. Portree (1,100) makes the best of the difficult communications of the island in linking its more populous northern half to the mainland, by the sea route to Mallaig and by road to the ferry over to the mainland at Kyle of Lochalsh.

Mull, with more than half the area of Skye, has less than a quarter of its population. Although a mountainous island, it has some very fertile land, and prosperous farms, but much of it is used for extensive sheep grazing, and so there is only a small remnant of former crofting. Tobermory has a well-protected harbour, and is linked to Oban by daily steamer, but for many islanders trade is hampered by bad communications.

To show still further contrasts in island economy, we can consider Islay's use of extensive, and easily cut, peat deposits as fuel for distilleries. This has given a relatively concentrated pattern of settlements in an almost empty rural setting. Dairying in Islay has been encouraged by a creamery at Port Charlotte, and in the smaller island of Coll there is a cheese factory. Dairying in both these islands has long been established by settlers from the lowlands, and crofting is not dominant in the present economy.

Tiree, though small, is a good example of the diversity of factors which give rise to the many variations in population and prosperity in the islands. It is not only of low altitude, but (unlike Coll, and many others) it is flat. It has less bare rock and moorland, and more fertile soil and sandy machair for the crofters' grazings. Although windswept and treeless, it has the sunniest month of May in the whole of Britain, and throughout the year it has 20 per cent. more sunshine than Stornoway. One indication of its prosperity is the density of cattle: the highest in any parish in the Highlands.

In great contrast to Tiree, and as a final example of the variation in conditions in the Hebrides, we may mention Jura ('Deer Island'), where the absence of soil, and the extensive bogs, have limited crofting to the east coast, and ensured that most of the island is true to its name as a land of sporting estates.

The Shetland Isles. The Shetland Isles, in the far north, are a more compact archipelago of a hundred islands and islets. Of these, only nineteen are inhabited, with a total population of 17,809, and a density of population of five persons per hundred acres. They are unique in many ways, most of all in position and in culture. Their remote northerly position is not always realised from the conventional placing of these islands in a convenient corner of the map of Scotland. They are, in fact, as far north as Leningrad or Labrador, and as far from Inverness as from Bergen. (We may not notice the extent of these islands, either, for a smaller scale is commonly used in the inset of the map. They are actually more extensive in land area than Fife, and more than twice the size of Dunbartonshire.)

The dominating fact of position has been responsible for their long history of Norse colonisation and culture, and this in turn has increased the sense of separation from the mainland of Scotland. It has also imposed two limitations on human activities: trade is restricted by transport costs; and the climate, although equable, is marred by cool summers and exposure to winter gales. Many of the islands are difficult of access, and many are too rocky for even the hardy Shetlander to till. (Yet the most northerly island of all – Unst – has still some thousand people, and a reputation for two famous products of the Islands – fine lace shawls, and ponies, or 'shelties'.) There are air services from Glasgow and Edinburgh each weekday to Sumburgh in Shetland, so that isolation is more a matter of expense than one of time and difficulty for traffic which can use this route. The difference in access and amenities in the south of the Islands is reflected in the concentration in the parish of Lerwick of over one-third of the population, and the continued growth of the population of this, the capital and only burgh.

As in Lewis, the soil lacks fertility, but is rich in peat. All but 7 per cent of the land is rough grazing, and only 3 per cent is arable. The only important crops are oats, hay, potatoes, and turnips. But there are a fifth of a million sheep, and this small Shetland animal is the basis of the hand-knitting industry (as well as providing wool for export). Even the Blackface sheep of the Scottish mainland would find these islands too bleak, but the native breed are out in all weathers, and these harsh conditions are said to favour the fine fibre for which they are famous. Cattle are much less important, and have decreased in numbers, but poultry have become more numerous recently, and there is an egg-packing station at Lerwick.

Although not mountainous, most of the islands have a wide variety of scenery, ice-eroded and weathered into rugged ridges and gullies, with many fresh-water lochs, and sea inlets, or voes. As in many of the Hebridean Islands, the sea, strong winds, and a quality of air and light, give their own character to the region; but in the Shetland Isles, long summer twilight is a reminder of the northerly latitude also. The crofts are scattered around the coasts, in the more protected valleys and voes. Unlike Lewis, Shetland's best soil, and most of its settlements, are found along the east, in coastal patches, each croft having a very restricted area of 'inbye' land, and often very poor quality common grazings (or 'scattalds').

The crofters of Shetland once supplemented their earnings by fishing in summer, but this practice is much less common today. Many of the islanders find their main employment in the herring fleet based on Lerwick and making landings there, at Scalloway, or further south. With smaller exports of cured fish, more is now taken to the mainland for sale. Some men go with the whaling boats to the Antarctic from September to May, and others serve in the Merchant Navy. The main problem for the fishing industry at Lerwick has been the cost of transport to the main markets, and much of the catch is sold to the large quick-freezing plant where herring (whole and filleted), kippers and white fish are processed ready for export to the main markets in the south.

Traditions also remain in the other occupations of Shetland, for many of the women and girls supplement their work on the croft by knitting, using traditional patterns, which have added greatly to the Island's prosperity. The northernmost isle has been mentioned for its shawls, and the southernmost isle – Fair Isle – has a special fame for its knitted goods. The finest part of the warm, silky fleece of the Shetland sheep is used for 'lacework' shawls, but almost all the knitwear industry today is in more substantial, machine-spun fibres, spun at Inverness from the Shetland wool, and returned for knitting in the Islands.

We may compare Shetland with the 'island' of Lewis. Although the former is an island group, while the latter is only a part of an island, they are comparable in many ways: in total population, and in average density of population; in the size of Stornoway (5,200), and Lerwick (5,900); but also, and of greater importance, in their economy. Both have their large areas of crofters' grazings, and small patches of cultivated land in the coastal districts; and both have the same two strong interests apart from crofting: fishing and textiles.

The West Highland Coastlands

On the coastal margins of the mainland, as in the Hebrides, there is a considerable variety of natural conditions, and of human activities. The land is most mountainous in the central coast area, from Gairloch to Oban, and here only a few peninsulas (e.g. Ardnamurchan and Morar), have any extent of lowland. This is in contrast to the north, where the higher mountains stand well back from the coast, and the south, where long peninsulas of lower, hilly, ground are found. In the north, cooler summers, and slightly colder winters are experienced, compared with the south; and although the mean annual rainfall of 40-50 inches is not heavy for the Highlands, exposure to the prevailing winds is more severe. But in the central coast area rainfall rises to about 70 inches annually, and winter temperatures are rather lower than elsewhere (about 39°F. in January, compared with 40°F. in the north, and 42° F. in south Kintyre).

More important than climatic variations are those of flatness and fertility, for farmland; and of access for marketing. In the north, there is a general lack of valleys with arable land and of machair for pasture, so that the wide extent of summer hill grazing is only partly used for cattle and sheep, and much of it is the domain of the deer. Several crofting townships are situated on raised beaches; some more prosperous crofts and sheep farms benefit from patches of limestone (e.g. Durness); a few straths occur with more fertile and more sheltered land, of use to farming in the lower reaches and forestry on the slopes; but elsewhere the coast is rocky and the moors are bare.

Throughout this northern coastal region there is the problem of communications. With no railways, and only one main road to Ullapool, both farming and fishing are restricted in trade links with the east and south, and tourists are fewer. Loch Shin and Strath Oykell provide secondary routes from the east, and there is a south-north road linking Durness and Ullapool, but only a few coastal settlements (notably the fishing port of Lochinver), are served, and many coastal peninsulas remain isolated. Most of the crofters and crofter-fishermen live on the coast, and here too are the few small villages where fishing and tourism are the main industries. Ullapool (500) is the one outstanding centre where the good harbour of Loch Broom joins with the shortest and best route across the North-west Highlands. It is one of the main ports for the herring fleets of the Minch, and boats from the east coast come here in summer to join with those from the western ports. Here too the tourist industry has grown recently.

The central coast area (from Gairloch to Oban), despite its more mountainous terrain, its deeply indented coast, and its wetter climate, is more densely peopled than the north. There is one main reason for this: the accessibility of the coast by rail and road at

14

several points, and particularly at the rail and boat centres of Oban, Fort William, Mallaig, and Kyle of Lochalsh. The population of Oban and Fort William alone exceeds that of the whole of the north-west coast. These centres are important for trade (e.g. sheep and cattle from the islands), for fishing, and for tourists. In all respects they serve not only the coastal area but also the Hebrides.

Sea as well as land communications stimulate industry in the region, where hydro-electricity, and some small mineral workings have been developed. The availability of water power for electricity was responsible for the aluminium works at Fort William and Kinlochleven. The alumina is brought from Burntisland, and the sheet and ingots are despatched by land routes to the centres of manufacture (such as Falkirk). Other industries have been stimulated by this development at Fort William. The town (2,700) has a radial pattern of land communications, and, as a regional centre for the west Highlands it serves a wide hinterland for trade and tourism. Reference has already been made to the importance of the new pulp and paper mill set up near Fort William (p. 47). This will increase the value of communications in the region as a whole. Kinlochleven (1,700) has a difficult situation for communications, and lacks room for expansion. Slate at Ballachulish, granite at Bonawe, and deposits of gravel and fine sand along this coastal area, have all been exploited at times, but are of little importance today.

Although Oban (6,800) has small industries (such as distilling and tweed manufacture), it is principally a holiday and tourist centre which has grown up in the last hundred years on a sheltered bay, facing the island of Mull. The smaller island of Kerrera gives more immediate shelter, and here there is a lobster packing station. Oban is more than twice the size of Fort William, and has attracted much of its population from the nearby region. It has influenced the farming of the immediate hinterland, for which it functions as a market for young dairy cattle.

Mallaig (600), like Oban, is a railhead and port for the Islands, but it is also a well established centre of herring fishing.

Despite these larger settlements, attracting and depending upon good routes, many areas are badly served by poor roads, as in the north-west, and in these remote districts there is little arable land, and few crofters. Much of the land is given up to deer forests, and some to the Forestry Commission, while along the coast there are small fishing townships, especially along the Inner Sound. Here and there a raised beach or strip of machair helps to support a dwindling community, but rugged relief, poor soil, and the remoteness of such peninsulas as Ardnamurchan discourage the full use of even the better pastures.

South of Oban, the West Highlands are broken into two main peninsulas: Knapdale-Kintyre, and Cowal. Although so close to the Central Lowlands, the region is not served by such good communications as the Oban-Fort William area, for no railways have been built here, and roads are circuitous. The western peninsula is easily crossed at Tarbert and Campbeltown by road, and at Lochgilphead by the Crinan Canal (the latter is very useful for fishing boats, yachts, and Clyde puffers). But otherwise east – west routes are very poor, and the good roads are limited to coastal culs-de-sac rather than forming through routes. The steamer services of the Firth of Clyde compensate to some extent for poor land communications, especially for holiday traffic to the east and south coasts of Cowal. For non-tourist interests these services are not adequate to maintain trade throughout the region.

The relief is broken, but not mountainous, and the climate is milder and less exposed than elsewhere in the West Highlands. These factors have combined with its position to encourage dairying in the coastal lowlands, and very little crofting remains today. The rougher land has for long been left to sheep, except where forestry has redeemed the decaying economy of poor pastures. Forestry is particularly important in the Cowal peninsula (with a Forestry School at Benmore), and dairying on the west and south of Kintyre.

Apart from the direct uses of the land, tourism and fishing form strong subsidiary interests: the former in the south of Cowal (from Dunoon to Kames), and the latter especially at Tarbert and Campbeltown, the two important bases for the Clyde herring fisheries. At Machrihanish coal seams occur and are still being mined, and at Campbeltown and Lochgilphead there are distilleries. Campbeltown, though so far by road from all large centres of population, has over 6,500 inhabitants. While fishing is its main strength, with a good harbour and a modern fleet of ring-net boats, it has a summer tourist industry; and besides the two distilleries and nearby coalmine there is a creamery to support Kintyre's dairy interests.

The islands of the Firth of Clyde – Arran, Bute, and the Cumbraes (together forming the County of Bute) – may be considered together with the south-east coast of Cowal. Though physically allied to the Highlands, this area is on the doorstep of the industrial Clyde valley, and, as the large merchant ships pass endlessly to and from the Glasgow docks, the small steamers ply from pier to pier, thronged in summer with holiday-makers. Though dairying is the main land use, most employment is found in catering for visitors at Dunoon (9,200), Rothesay (7,650), and many other resorts.

II. THE CENTRAL HIGHLANDS

This core of the Highland Zone dominates the whole region as a great barrier, repelling man in almost all his activities. It is an area of great watersheds, rising to 3,000 or 4,000 feet, and of deeply dissected plateaux, in which the glens are narrow and steep walled. It is equally an area of great climatic difficulty. While in the east rainfall may be lower than that of the western coasts (below 40 inches annually in some of the glens), there are wide extents of mountain and plateau with over a hundred inches per annum, and Glen Quoich, the wettest place in Britain, has up to 225 inches a year. The winters are cold, with heavy snow and frost, and cold air slips from the mountains into the glens (where shadow may also lower temperatures for many months in the year). Spring comes much later to the west and south, and summers are cool in all but the most favoured spots.

Peat moor and bog covers the greatest area of the region, and is broken only by forests and pasture on less precipitous slopes, and richer alluvial areas. Thus the predominant usage is not agricultural, even in the pastoral sense, but recreational: a deserted land of deer forest and Nature Reserve, reawakened each season for activities such as shooting, fishing, ski-ing and climbing. Deer forests in Scotland occupy two and a half million acres of land (about the same area as that of the counties of Inverness and Caithness combined), well over half being in Inverness and Ross and Cromarty, and the rest almost entirely in Sutherland, Argyll, Perth and Aberdeen counties. Only about one-third the area of deer forest is estimated as rough grazing, carrying stock, and there is only one sheep to every 23 acres of deer forest.

Two types of nature conservancy require mention. One is the Nature Reserve, intended to maintain, with as little change as possible, the land and life of large tracts of Scottish countryside. Much the largest in Britain, and one of the largest in Europe is that of the Cairngorms reserve, which extends for 62 square miles and includes the three highest summits. Although overlapping with the sporting estates, the preservation of wild life is the primary aim. In some ways similar in their regard for conservancy, the national Forest Parks, while safeguarding the forested areas which they include, make provision for the recreational interests of the public. The Argyll Forest Park, for instance, comprises four or five forest areas and higher land, including The Cobbler, and some open spaces suitable for camping. The Queen Elizabeth Forest Park stretches from Loch Lomond to Loch Vennachar, and half the area is made up of lochs and unforested mountain.

Crofting communities are small, and very isolated. Usually they occur in the wider river valleys, and loch-delta areas, with summer grazing on the lower slopes. Often a morainic area of better drained, and relatively fertile, land intercedes between the steep slopes of the mountain and the loch or bog of the lower levels, and here a few crofts may cling beside the roadway or near to the forest which brings some subsidiary seasonal employment. The roads in the deep Highland glens do not merely provide employment in their main-tenance, but enable the crofter to work at a greater distance from his home (a function which is partly assumed by the sea on the West Highland coast and in the Islands), and since subsistence is not possible from the croft today, the road is also the necessary link with markets and shops. Thus the survival of crofting depends in this region upon the careful use of the small islands of fertility, upon subsidiary work, and upon access to road (or, more rarely, railway). In the south of Glen More, forestry and public services, such as road maintenance, take precedence in the subsidiary occupations of the crofter, but conditions vary widely in the opportunities offered throughout the whole of the Highlands.

There is some agricultural use (other than crofting), of this central mountain core, where conditions enable the more extensive pasturing of stock (e.g. around Loch Arkaig). The use of moorland for sheep pasture increases where lower farmland is approached, and there is good summer grazing for cattle in some districts, but this must be managed in combination with the provision of winter foodstuffs. At either end of Glen More this has been achieved in two large, ranch-like, farms, and in some other areas on a smaller scale, by farmers who have the advantage of lowland arable and pasture, as well as rough grazing in the mountains. This is a form of land use which bridges the central Highlands and the eastern straths and glens.

Through the heart of this mountain core runs Glen More, and here three special human consequences can be traced from the deep and narrow rift of lowland which runs from coast to coast. The first, and most fundamental, is that of communications, for this has been a factor in all other activities, and one of a long historical development. The strategic value of the route gave rise to castles and forts (e.g. Inverness, Fort William, and Fort Augustus), and while the most important terminal route centres are not within the region now being considered, Invergarry, Fort Augustus, Invermoriston, and Drumnadrochit deserve special mention as route junctions linking the main road from north-east to south-west with the glens which reach into the Highlands on either side. There is no railway to supplement the main route from Inverness to Fort William, but the Caledonian Canal, which joins the Moray Firth, Loch Ness, Loch Oich, Loch Lochy and Loch Linnhe, is important for small craft (especially fishing boats and small oil-tankers), which would otherwise be forced to take the longer and more dangerous voyage around the north of Scotland.

Good communications have combined with the steep sided walls of the Glen, and the high rainfall of the region, to encourage the very early use of water-power for the generation of electricity. Fort William and Kinlochleven have already been mentioned as centres for producing aluminium from alumina by hydro-electricity. Foyers, on the eastern bank of Loch Ness is the third centre for this industry, and was the earliest to be established (1895).

The third result of the special physical conditions of Glen More is that of land use. Both farming and forestry benefit from the degree of climatic protection and from the ease of access in this corridor. While farming has been limited in extent by the large area of fresh water throughout most of the Glen, forestry has taken advantage of the slopes on each side.

III. THE EASTERN STRATHS AND GLENS

This marginal area of deep valleys and intervening Highland spurs borders the central mountain core to the east and south-east, and is marked off as a transitional land between mountain and plain. Just as the central Highlands repel the economic advances of man, so the east coast plains attract them, and therefore this transitional zone looks to the east and south for its immediate links in land use, communications, and industry. Although the use of mountain pastures for summer grazing has been referred to, the main agricultural pursuits of the valley farms are associated with the more intensive stock and arable lands of the coastal plains. The Perthshire valleys, especially of the Tay basin, and those of the rivers Dee, Don, and Spey intrude sinuous extensions of farmland between the barren moorlands.

This fringe of relatively prosperous agriculture depends upon the more level land and more fertile soil, of course, but also upon the drier and sunnier climate. While these factors are insufficient to enable farmers to grow crops or fatten cattle extensively, they are able to use high proportions of rough grazing, and some permanent pasture and arable, for rearing young stock. The Highland region, as a whole, accounts for almost a half of Scotland's hill sheep farms, and while some use the central mountain core, most are marginally situated in this eastern and southern area. Even more typical of these straths and glens than the hill sheep farms, are the stock rearing farms, in which there is more use of arable land for feeding in winter, and young cattle play an important part in the farm economy. These are small family farms with little mechanisation, and with only about 30 acres of arable land (on the average half the arable is used for rotation grass, and a third for cereals), but they are very different from the croft with its two or three cattle and dozen sheep, especially in its provision of full employment, and in its independence of common grazings.

Among interests common to the Highlands as a whole, forestry, like farming, seeks the protection of these straths and glens, and, while hydro-electricity depends on the mountain core for its catchment areas, many power stations and power lines make use of the eastern and southern valleys. Tourists are also attracted to these accessible margins of the higher mountain region. Pitlochry, Ballater, and Grantown-on-Spey are three centres among many which have a special fame for holiday-makers, and sports enthusiasts.

Most settlements in the straths and glens are shopping and market centres for the agricultural population: centres for many scattered communities. Often they are at the confluence of rivers, and two of the three holiday centres quoted above – Grantown and Pitlochry – are route junctions of this type, while the third, Ballater, stands at the edge of an alluvial plain. We may compare these smaller settlements with the foothill towns which stand as gateways to the eastern and southern lowlands: Callander, Crieff, Dunkeld to the south; and Huntly and Rothes further north, for example.

In both Dee and Don valleys, the fertile stretches alternate with poorer, and more restricted valley lands, so that a number of local market centres are strung along each valley, linked by the main roads (on both sides of the Dee valley). The importance of these centres is lessened by the strong 'pull' of Aberdeen as the commercial metropolis of a large region.

In such a transitional region between mountain and lowland there can be no firm boundary. The hinterlands of the foothill towns, such as Blairgowrie and Huntly, stretch well back into the Highlands, yet are not confined to it (as are those of Kingussie or Aberfeldy).

Two areas of transition require special mention: the Inverness area, and Strath Spey between Grantown and Fochabers. **Inverness (30,000)**, has a unique position, for it links Glen More with the eastern lowlands, and the main road and railway through the Grampians (from Kingussie to Pitlochry via the passes of Drumochter and Killiecrankie), joins Inverness to Strath Spey and the Tay basin. This convergence of routes is augmented by the termination of the Caledonian Canal. As a market centre and county town, it has a wide hinterland – almost entirely within the Highlands. As a summer centre for tourists (to whom it is the capital of the Highlands), it has an even wider catchment area. Its industries are small: distilleries, tweed mills, and spinning mills for Hebridean and Shetland wool, and some engineering; but it is a busy and thriving burgh.

The lower Spey valley has, on a much greater scale than Inverness, an interest in the distillation of whisky. The Highland malt distilleries are widely spread in the eastern and southern valleys of the Highlands, and a few are in the west, but the greatest concentration is between Dufftown and Rothes (and continues to Elgin and Forres on the lowlands). These distilleries use only barley to make their malt, and from this comes the spirit which is used by the blenders in the Central Lowlands. Although coke must be imported, the use of peat, and the need for pure water, helps to explain the general distribution in the Highland Zone. The importance of barley in the north-east lowlands also favours the concentration in the Spey valley. The maintenance of well known distilleries is also a matter of traditional skill and knowledge. No two distilleries produce the same spirit, and conservatism must be expected in such a matter of taste.

North of Inverness, this foothill region is reduced to a smaller terrain, for the character of the central Highlands, with its extensive sheep farms, deer forests, and occasional crofts, continues in Ross and Cromarty and Sutherland to the coast. Glen Cassley, Strath Oykell and the other valleys of the north, are not comparable with the broader lowlands of Tay or Dee. Forestry has, however, brought some employment here too, as has hydro-electricity (Loch Shin); and these valleys offer routes for roads joining east and west coasts. Market centres such as Lairg, are as extensive, if not as prosperous, in hinterland as those further south. The narrow coastal lowland alternates with the east coast plains, and is most restricted to the north of Tain. Except near Dornoch and Brora there is little flat land for farming and the settlements are small fishing villages, and market centres for the hill sheep farms (e.g. Helmsdale). Brora (800) is an exception in possessing the one small coal mine in the north-east, and it has a distillery, woollen mills and brickworks too.

At Dounreay in north-west Caithness a large, fast-working, atomic reactor has been built. Closeness to the sea for waste disposal, and for water for cooling, and the safety of a remote location explain the choice of site. Apart from transient labour during construction there has been a more permanent increase in Thurso's population. At Altnabreac, also in western Caithness, a project for producing power from peat (and land reclamation) has failed to develop. It is indicative of the difficulty of harnessing the local resources of the Highlands, unless the needs of the country as a whole are involved – as they are at Dounreay.

XVII · THE HIGHLAND ZONE

THE NORTH-EAST LOWLANDS

THIS region is not easily seen as a single unit on the map of Scotland, and it shows considerable variety in its geography, but it has very strong characteristics of its own. Its northerly latitude separates it from the Central Lowlands, and between Stonehaven and Aberdeen only a narrow coastal corridor links the two lowlands. Yet from Aberdeen to Orkney is half Scotland's total range of latitude, so that the factor of isolation increases considerably between the two extremities. Its position to the east of the Highlands cuts it off very effectively from the coastal and insular lowlands of the west although the Orkney Isles are a major exception, where only the sea intervenes, and the Moray lowlands have their link with the west in Glen More. Its coastal character and its low elevation are clear in all areas; only in Aberdeenshire do the lowlands reach more than 20 miles inland, and wherever a thousand feet is approached the transitional region of the eastern Highlands can be said to begin.

In climate this part of Scotland is unique, with its dry, cool, yet sunny weather. Though mean temperatures in January and July do not differ greatly from those of the west coast, cold winds in winter, and longer sunshine in summer, give the effect of a more extreme climate. Almost everywhere, mean annual rainfall is less than 30 inches.

The land use is very distinct from that of the Highlands, for here there is farming of a more continuous and intensive type, noted for stock rearing and fattening, with little or no crofting or hill sheep farming. The region as a whole has some two-thirds of Scotland's stock rearing and feeding farms, and over a third of its 'cropping' farms (farms which are most concerned with the sale of crops rather than stock). A strong feature in the farming of the region is the use of a six year rotation of crops: cereal, roots, cereal, 3 years grass; with modifications to suit local conditions (e.g. where the sale of crops is important the rotation may be shortened by the use of rotation grass – or 'leys', for two instead of three years).

Fishing is an enterprise shared with all Scottish coastlands, but in the north-east it is most fully integrated as an industry – full time, and of prime importance to the region.

Communications and towns are neither as crowded and over-strained as in the Central Lowlands, nor as attenuated and sporadic as in the Highlands, but well-spaced burghs are firmly linked by road

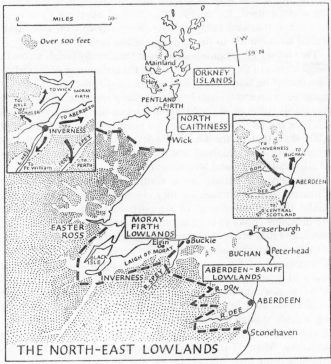

FIG. 74

from Aberdeen to Thurso, and sea and air routes augment the mainland services, and extend them to the Orkney Isles.

Despite advantages which seem so outstanding in comparison with the Highlands, the north-east of Scotland is not naturally well endowed. Soil and climate are only conducive to prosperous farming in restricted areas. The fishing industry has had many setbacks, and the competition of big firms operating from English and foreign ports has set it a major problem today. There is very little mineral wealth. As a detached fragment of those plains which encircle the North Sea, it compares most closely with Scandinavia in the need for great human effort to overcome natural deficiencies. With some Norse blood, and with as great a determination as that found in Scandinavia itself, the people of north-east Scotland have established, and maintain today, a lively prosperity of their own, and a special contribution to the economy of the nation.

The Orkney Isles. Some 6 miles from Duncansby Head, across the rough waters of the Pentland Firth, lie the main'group of the Orkney Isles encircling Scapa Flow, and further on still, the North Isles are scattered in an archipelago broken by many sounds and firths. With two-thirds the area of the Shetland Isles, it has 1,000 more people (18,700), but its loss over the last ten years has also been greater by 1,000 than that of the Shetland Isles. About two-thirds of these Orcadians live in Mainland, and over one-quarter in the two burghs of Kirkwall (4,300) and Stromness (1,500).

Physically the islands are a continuation of the lowlands of Caithness, and in climate too they are similar. Winters are a little milder than those of most of the north-east plains, but summers are definitely cooler (54° F. in July, compared with 57° F. in Aberdeen), and they are very exposed to high winds.

Only a very small number of crofters remain in what has long been a stronghold of family farms. They are small holdings (average size is 71 acres,* and 60 per cent have less than 50 acres), but great effort has made them economically successful. The land has called for much reclamation in the clearing of heather and stones, and the draining of fields, though low rainfall reduces the problem of surface water.

The type of farming in Orkney resembles closely that of Aberdeenshire. Most of the islands concentrate on stock rearing and fattening with little interest in the sale of crops. But this is not pastoral farming so much as 'fodder' farming, for in Orkney the arable area is more than four times as great as that under permanent grass, despite recent decreases in tilled land. This intensive farming can be illustrated by the many tractors at work on farms where little or no hired labour is used. Since 1946 the number of tractors has increased from less than 700 to over 2,000 – compared with about 500 in the Shetland Isles.

*42 acres of crops and grass; 29 acres of rough grazing.

In Hoy, and the south of Mainland, rearing, rather than fattening of stock, is most important; and near Kirkwall and other coastal parts of Mainland small herds of dairy cattle are kept. But the emphasis is generally on beef cattle, and, as one would expect, the important crops are oats and turnips. There is a very considerable poultry industry, and a large export of eggs. About 7 per cent of Scotland's egg-laying poultry are in the Orkney Isles, which are third only to Aberdeenshire and Ayrshire in this industry.

The successful stock farming of Orkney owes much to immigrants from Aberdeenshire, who came here in the later nineteenth century, but today the Islands are losing many people to the mainland of Scotland, and the drift south occurs within the islands as well as beyond them. This is to be expected where transport costs and isolation from many modern amenities increase northwards. In this loss of population the Orkney Isles have a common bond with the Highlands, and, though so different in most other ways, they are a part of the region known as the 'Crofting Counties'.

Fishing is of little importance – apart from shell fishing – compared with its counterpart in Shetland, but there are a few hundred motor vessels based on the Islands, with about 400 men employed – including some crofter fishermen. During and between the two wars Scapa Flow was a most important Naval base.

North Caithness. Apart from Thurso, Caithness has a similar population to Orkney, but it has a larger area of mountain and moor to the south. It is only the north of the county, where most of the people live, that comes within the region of Scotland being considered. Here it is as flat and treeless as most of Orkney, with small family farms, and fields separated by the same grey flags which are used in the buildings. Shelly boulder clay gives a fertile soil and arable is again extensive compared with permanent grass. As in Orkney, oats and root crops occupy most of the tilled land, and decrease of tillage has been less marked here. In stock rearing and fattening there is much more emphasis on sheep, and less on cattle. Poultry are a much less notable feature of farming than in Orkney.

Stock rearing is the main farming activity, with fattening in the north, and some dairying around the Wick and Thurso areas. Crofting communities are again in a minority, but in the extreme north-east of the county, away from the Wick-Thurso corridor, crofting is more common, as it is in the south of Caithness. Fishing is a subsidiary occupation for some crofters (in 1962, about 40 of the 300 fishermen in the Wick district were crofters: in Orkney and Shetland about 300 were crofters in a total of 1,200 fishermen).

Wick (7,400), the county town, stands at the head of a shallow bay, and fishing and fish processing are the main activities. Herring have been the main catch (through July and August, but also in February), but with the decline in the export of herring, seine-net fishing for white fish has become more attractive. Shell fish now take second place to the demersal landings along the Caithness coast. Thurso, with a population which has grown from little more than 3,000 in 1951 to over 8,000 in 1961 has been referred to in relation to Dounreay (see p. 209), but as well as this new dormitory function, Thurso is a market town and has small manufacturing industries (e.g. hosiery), as well as shell fish processing. Scrabster is notable for white fish, and for its ferry link with Stromness. Other small industries of the Caithness towns include hosiery, boat-building, and engineering.

The Moray Firth Lowlands. These are formed of two peninsulas bounded by the drowned valleys of Dornoch, Cromarty, and Beauly Firths, and the coastal plain from Inverness to the river Spey. It is more protected than the windy, treeless lowlands further north, and has generally milder winters and earlier harvests than Caithness to the north, or Banff and Aberdeen to the east. When we add to this its dryness (much of it has less than 25 inches of rain per annum), its high amounts of sunshine, and the many level areas of good soil, its agricultural prosperity is easily understood. But good communications are a further asset, for the coastal road and railway provide direct services, with branch routes in the less accessible Black Isle.

In farming this region is distinct from the rest of north-east Scotland in its interest in growing crops for sale rather than for fodder, especially in Easter Ross, the coasts of the Black Isle and the Laigh of Moray (from Nairn to Fochabers). There are variations and specialisations, of course, such as the winter fattening of the North-Country Cheviot sheep, which – like the breed itself – is associated with Easter Ross; and, in the same area, barley and seed potatoes are very important. North of Dingwall, and in the hilly centre of the Black Isle, there is rougher stock-rearing land, and near Inverness some dairy farming, but otherwise the predominant type of farming is that in which arable is the major interest, with stock rearing or fattening a strong secondary objective. On these farms, which are larger than most in the north-east, oats occupy a large proportion of the total acreage, while wheat is scarcely grown at all. Barley is an important crop in this sheltered, dry region, especially along the southern shore of the Moray Firth. In the county of Moray, barley occupies a larger fraction of the arable than elsewhere in the north-east. The climatic advantages are also clear in the high yield of barley per acre. Nairn closely rivals Moray in proportion of land under barley, but the yield per acre is lower. Fruit and vegetables are important crops in Moray; small fruit and, to a greater extent, vegetables occupy a significant acreage (raspberries and carrots are notable products).

The coastal lowlands are fringed by raised beaches, and in some areas by stretches of sand. The Culbin sands, north-west of Forres, are a striking example of dune formation. Here the sand has been blown inland by strong winds, causing devastation in the past, but plantations of fir trees have been established to prevent further encroachment and much of the area has been reclaimed. This low coastline contrasts with the line of cliffs north of Elgin, where fishing villages continue the pattern of settlements which are found along the coasts of Banff and Aberdeen. This is not the most important part of the north-east region for fishing, for it lacks the closeness to the North Sea grounds, and the Moray Firth is easily fished from further east, but Lossiemouth is fifth in the list of Scottish ports for white fish, the whole catch being made by seine-net boats.

Elgin (12,000), an old cathedral city, reflects the prosperous farmland, forestry and distilling interests of the Laigh of Moray in such industries as woollens, whisky and timber. Equally, administration and social amenities reflect its central position in the lowland. Nairn (4,900), and Forres (4,800) share the west of this rich hinterland; and Nairn, like Lossiemouth, attracts many visitors in summer, the older fishing village being overshadowed by the newer town which looks to road and rail routes to provide the holiday traffic.

Still further west, Tain and Dingwall serve as market centres too, but with more immediate Highland hinterland. The valleys of the Spey and Findhorn provide routes through richer countryside (with some river terraces providing good agricultural land), before the

hill sheep country is reached, and Elgin and Forres gain some of
their trade from these inland areas. Dingwall's routes to the west,
via Achnasheen to the Kyle of Lochalsh, and to Ullapool, pass
almost immediately into moorland, with extensive rough pastures
and isolated crofts. Dingwall (3,750) is a railway junction as well as
a road centre and market for the fertile lands of Easter Ross.

The Aberdeen-Banff Lowlands. This is both the most easterly and
the most southerly extent of the north-east plains. The Buchan
plateau, or peneplain, is a few hundred feet above sea-level, forming
a flat treeless promontory of the Scottish mainland, and behind it
a fringing foothill area stretches from the north coast around Banff
to the east coast around Aberdeen. The two important valleys of
the rivers Dee and Don in the south of this foothill region have a
lesser counterpart in the valley of the Deveron and in Strathbogie
in the north, and the watershed between the two pairs of valleys
continues to the coast as the highest and northernmost part of
Buchan.

Despite its more southerly latitude, summers are cooler and
damper than those of Nairn and Moray, for it has a double coastal
aspect and comparative lack of protecting highlands. There is, then,
poorer harvesting weather for cereal crops. It is, however, the stock
farming region most noted for the development of the two breeds
of cattle, Aberdeen-Angus, and Aberdeen Shorthorn, which provide
most prime beef for the Scottish market.

The enterprise shown in developing these breeds of cattle has also
been shown in the improvement of a stony, thin soiled, and badly
drained land. The acidity of the soil, which can be tolerated by the
fodder crops – oats, turnips, and grass – has been reduced by liming
where barley is grown, and many lime kilns are found here. But
Aberdeenshire and Banffshire have one and a half times as much land
in oats as in barley, despite the general trend throughout Scotland
of increasing the barley acreage at the expense of oats. The region
resembles the Caithness and Orkney areas in its emphasis on stock
rearing and fattening, and in its use of poorer land. This poorer land,
with more rough grazing, maintains young cattle and sheep, with
little arable and therefore little fattening of stock. Such farms have
been described as most common in the eastern straths and glens of
the Highlands, but here they overlap, in the foothills which fringe
the Buchan plateau, with the more dominant stock-fattening farms.

In some districts the farmers grow crops for sale as well as fodder, especially in lower Banffshire, Huntly, Garioch, Alford, and Deeside areas, and here less turnips are grown. These farms are often larger than the small family farms, which concentrate entirely on stock and fodder. Although beef cattle are most important, sheep and poultry both play a large part in the farming economy. Over a quarter of Scotland's nine million poultry are in Aberdeenshire. Some are reared on farms which specialise in poultry, with a thousand or more birds on each farm (these are small compared with most specialist poultry farms), but most poultry are found as small flocks on the farms which rear, or rear and fatten, stock. Near Aberdeen, and along the coastal plain to the north, dairy farms predominate, as one might expect near a large city, and among other specialisations in farming some localities are noted for seed potatoes.

The Buchan area has no large towns inland, the market centres standing back at the junction of road and rail routes with the valleys in the foothill fringe between Aberdeen and Banff, and in a further series where the Highlands approach more closely to the lowland, between Banchory and Keith. Turiff is a centre for the richer land of the Deveron valley, and Huntly for the alluvium of Strathbogie, while Inverurie is situated in a wide opening of the middle Don basin. Beside their market interests, many of the small towns of the region continue to have traditional industries, but no longer use local water-power, nor limit themselves to local raw materials and the demands of the home market. Thus we find paper and flour mills at Inverurie (5,150), woollens at Keith (4,200) and knitwear at Huntly (4,000). In both textile and paper mills specialisation ensures a high quality in their products.

The long coastline from the mouth of the river Dee to that of the river Spey has given ample opportunity for establishing good harbours, and the region combines proximity to the nearer fishing grounds with the strongest land communications of any area north of the boundary fault. Aberdeen is the outstanding fishing port of the region, but it is so much more than this that a fuller, and separate, description of the city is given below. Peterhead (12,500) and Fraserburgh (10,500) have advantages in attracting smaller boats from the many harbours east of the river Spey, as well as giving their own fleets the advantages of good road services. Fraserburgh

15

has the heaviest landings of herring of any Scottish port, and records a considerable catch of white fish, brought in by seine-netters, and of crabs. Peterhead (once the centre of whaling) has much smaller landings of both herring and white fish, and with most of its granite quarries closed it has come to depend increasingly on secondary industries: distilling, food-canning, engineering and textiles. Food processing and engineering are of some importance in Fraserburgh also. Buckie (7,700) and Macduff (3,500) are notable for white fish landings, and at Buckie 'Norway lobsters' have become a valuable catch (see p. 42). Buckie, Sandhaven, and Peterhead share an interest in building small fishing boats and yachts, though Aberdeen remains the dominant ship-building centre in the north-east.

Aberdeen. The city of Aberdeen, with a population of 185,000, is the largest settlement in the north of Scotland. It is, in effect, the fusion of the old town, which evolved around the mouth of the river Don, and the newer part, which developed along the lower section of the river Dee. The city is the accepted capital of the North, the major focal point for a very large surrounding area.

Despite, and probably because of, their aloofness from the other large cities, and the main industrial areas of Scotland, the Aberdonians engage themselves in pursuits that, being in part peculiar to their environment, are now well nigh permanently associated with the city. In its townsfolk, as well as in the fair appearance of its granite buildings, there is an individuality about Aberdeen that is not repeated elsewhere in Scotland. Well removed though it is from coal-mining areas, Aberdeen is by no means an unimportant industrial centre and, both in respect of size of population and in area, its city status is fully merited.

The reputation of Aberdeen as a fishing port is not over-rated. It is, by far, the most important fishing port in Scotland, and its trawler fleet works as far away as Newfoundland. The landings of fish are invariably very heavy – white fish all the year round and herring in the summer – and the proximity of the fish market to the main railway depot is a convenience essential for the prompt despatch of fish in ice to all parts of Great Britain by fish express as well as by fast lorry.

Throughout the fishing industry there are great ramifications, and many are those who depend on the trade, apart from the fishermen themselves – ship-builders and repairers, net, barrel and box makers, ice and fish-meal factory workers, curers, provision and gear merchants, as well as the host of fish-workers, male and female alike, who handle the fish at some stage in its transit to the retailer and customer. The extensive lay-out of the present fish market and the organisation of the morning fish auctions prior to distribution make it hard to think of a former primitive fishing settlement on the sand-enveloped channel of the river Dee.

At Rubislaw, within the city, an enormous supply of bright, grey granite has been worked for over 200 years, while at Kemnay, and other quarries near to Aberdeen, further workings have been developed in the last 100 years. The attractive and durable buildings and causeways of Aberdeen are a sufficient index of the value of granite, but it is also important in monumental work, and in the construction of bridges, docks and jetties. Of all its uses, building is now most important, though slabs, rather than blocks, are used for façades, and synthetic granite (made with cement from granite dust and chips) is in great demand. Largely mechanised nowadays, the industry needs fewer masons and is not a big employer of labour. However, granite is more than a source of employment: it is part of Aberdeen's import and export trade, though exports have greatly decreased.

Not so convenient is the source of raw material for the shipbuilding and engineering pursuits of the city. Despite this handicap, some dozen vessels – trawlers, tugs, coasters, bulk-carriers and tankers – are launched every year, while a great amount of ship-repairs is carried out. In engineering, the variety of activities, as well as the smallness of firms rather than the magnitude of the industry is noteworthy. Cranes, ploughs, tools, aerial cableways and mechanical excavators are products made in Aberdeen.

The manufacture of paper has, for long, been an important industry in and around the city and Aberdeen is now one of the leading centres for paper in Great Britain. Access to sea transport of raw and finished materials fostered the trade and the abundance of water, at first for power and now for processing, determined the siting of the mills on the banks of the rivers Dee and Don. Besides textile trimmings and rags, esparto grass and wood pulp are used in making all sorts of paper – writing and mapping paper, newsprint and paper board. Bales of wood pulp are brought from Scandinavia, while Spain and North Africa are the sources of the esparto grass.

Longer still has been the association of the textile industry with the populace of the city. It gives employment to a large number of women workers. Flax and wool are the two natural fibres which are now processed. The former, imported from Russia and the Baltic, is used in the manufacture of strong canvas hosepiping, tarpaulins, sacks and webbing – from raw material to finished goods. Scottish and Australasian wools are woven into good class heavy tweed, jumpers and stockings.

The links between Aberdeen and its county and neighbouring counties are very strong in more than one respect. By several bridges, the earliest over the Don in 1320 and over the Dee in 1530, important routes, reaching out in three directions from the city, make Aberdeen the centre of exchange for the very productive agricultural counties of the north-east. Not an inconsiderable part of its life is in its produce and grain markets, its livestock marts, its weekly and seasonal sales, its seed and agricultural implement sales.

By sea the communications of Aberdeen stretch further afield. It is the supply port for the Orkney and Shetland Isles, the great stacks of Orkney egg boxes to be seen on the quays at Aberdeen being one of the main items of shipment. Imports are more than six times the tonnage of exports, and fuel – both coal and oil – is foremost in this side of Aberdeen's trade. Other notable imports are of wood-pulp and sawn softwood timber from the Baltic and North America, esparto grass from North Africa, and phosphates from Nauru Islands (central Pacific) and North Africa. Exports include oats, fishmeal, seed potatoes, fertilisers and paper. Coastwise shipping carries nearly three times the tonnage of foreign trade, and exports abroad account for less than 2 per cent of Aberdeen's total trade tonnage. But this is not the full measure of the trade of the city: there is always a large despatch, by rail and lorry, of its products to many British ports, and in particular to Glasgow, for transhipment abroad.

Although the foundations of Aberdeen's cultural and ecclesiastical life were laid early in the history of the town, it was in the eighteenth century that the significant social and economic development took place. Then, apart from the extension of the town, the opening of new thoroughfares, the reclamation of its loch marshlands (around Loch Street) and the improvement to the harbour and navigational channel, initial steps were taken to give permanence to the industries in which Aberdeen is now principally engaged. But, even today, the city continues to enlarge its boundaries by the creation of large suburban housing estates. It enjoys a very good share of the holiday traffic of Scotland. In its urban setting, its fine beach and promenade, and in the excellence of the river scenery of the neighbourhood, Aberdeen provides a variety of attractions to visitors and it is always popular as a summer resort.

XVIII · THE CHANGING ASPECTS OF
THE ECONOMY OF SCOTLAND

WHILE references have been made in previous chapters to some of the recent developments in Scotland's economy, there is a need for a more connected account of such developments, and for comment on their significance. It is true that, in Scotland, as in most other lands, the eventual outcome of present changes remains in doubt, and an element of prophecy is inevitable in assessing the direction in which current trends will develop. But, so long as this speculative context is remembered, the attempt to portray present plans and trends is justified by their importance for the immediate future of the country.

There is one region of special concern in Scotland's economy – the Central Lowlands – and this region is given the major share of attention below. But beyond this regional focus there is a less recognised scene of change in the country, at once more widely spread in its effects and more difficult to define, viz. the agricultural economy. An attempt has been made therefore to summarise some of the shifts of emphasis which can be noted in farming and land-use. But it is not to be inferred from this concentration of attention – regional and thematic – that other areas and industries are static, much less stagnant, in the mid-twentieth century: only that earlier references in the text must suffice where 'change' is still fragmentary or ill-defined.

THE CENTRAL LOWLANDS

Few people can fail to notice the great changes taking place in the Central Lowlands. Within the last few years, there has been a profound transformation in the appearance of many parts of this region. From Dundee in the east to Hunterston on the Ayrshire coast, changes far greater than those at any other time in this century have been accomplished with astonishing rapidity. There has been a mid-century industrial and social revolution. A store of experience, derived from many previous decades, set it in motion, and the renaissance is by no means at an end. The projects and undertakings now completed or envisaged are designed to improve and develop the economy of Scotland. They are far reaching in character and forward looking. Without such changes, there would be little or no economic growth, and the Central Lowlands would become an industrial backwater.

Scotland's Economic Heritage

The origins of Scotland's industrial expansion are well known. Industry developed most strongly in the Central Lowlands. Here, in remarkable compactness, were coal and iron ore (both essential in the decades during which steam and iron were supreme), and navigable firths to support commercial enterprise. While the expanding British Empire provided a market for Scottish products, and there were yet few rivals in the range of manufactures for which the country was famous, expansion continued. But in the twentieth century, the traditional industries, particularly ship-building and other heavy engineering industries, experienced mixed prosperity and recession. During the two world wars, Scottish yards and workshops made a significant contribution to the nation's war efforts. Between the wars and after the second war, Scotland found itself over-dependent on industries which provided little scope for increased growth. Faced with strong world competition, and with new manufacturing techniques developed more fully and freely among these competitors, the traditional industries suffered a serious contraction. Phases of acute unemployment ensued, and, despite a rise in population, the pace of industrial enterprise has lagged behind that of other regions in Great Britain. Loss of people through emigration to England and elsewhere has been an unwelcome indicator of this lack of industrial vitality, and a higher than average level of unemployment continues to act as a reminder of Scotland's disadvantage in the competition to gain new industries.

The Programme for Development. To secure a faster economic advance, a major programme of development and growth has been drawn up.* It contains proposals for the deliberate, planned, regional reconstruction and modernisation of the Central Lowlands, where three quarters of the population and nine tenths of the industry

*Central Scotland, A Programme for Development and Growth, H.M.S.O. 1963.

EMPLOYMENT IN GROWTH

ESTIMATED NUMBERS IN THOUSANDS FOR 1963 AND INCREASE OR DECREASE FOR 1964

1963 : 1964

1. 2.

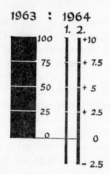

(1. Estimated change : 1963-64;
2. Potential increase from projects
started or approved at
June 1964)

Development Districts

New Towns

TRUNK ROADS & MOTORWAYS

To be completed by 1970

To be initiated by 1970

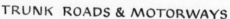

A: Irvine   B: Vale of Leven   C: East Kilbrie

FIG. 75

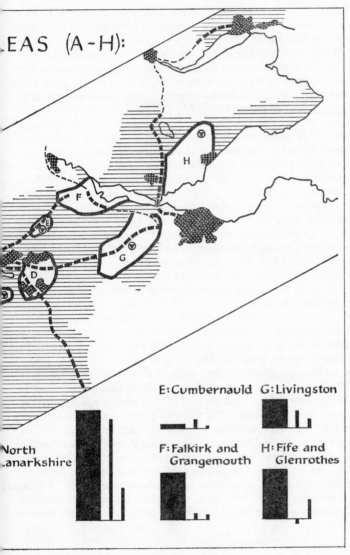

EAS (A-H):

E:Cumbernauld   G:Livingston

North
Lanarkshire

F:Falkirk and
  Grangemouth

H:Fife and
  Glenrothes

Fɪɢ. 75

of Scotland are concentrated. Such a venture is entirely new in that it embodies a more forthright attitude of governmental economic planning than has ever been attempted hitherto.

Modernisation is the overall keynote of these fundamental proposals. First, growth areas have been delimited, without restriction to the older civic boundaries, to act as focal points for rapid and substantial expansion. Within them, a wide range of industrial enterprise will be fostered by public and private finance.* It should be realised that Central Scotland, as a whole, has already gained a high rate of public service investment: over a quarter of a billion pounds in the last two years, or 11 per cent of Britain's total of such investment gained for the benefit of $7\frac{1}{2}$ per cent of Britain's population. Increased public investment of this magnitude will help to provide new or improved 'infrastructure' services such as roads, docks, airports, power and water supply, repair and revival of older industrial areas, as well as housing and other domestic schemes. All such services form an integral part of an efficient industrial economy. A supply of manpower, including highly skilled labour, equally essential to any plan of economic growth, has not been overlooked. Within and beyond the growth areas, improved communications will enable labour to move to and from work more easily. There are to be greater facilities for technical and other specialised types of training and re-training. New Towns, now in existence or taking shape, are designed to house the workers in the young industries which are springing to full life in the Central Lowlands.

Growth areas (Fig. 75) are of three types: the New Towns themselves; the growing urban areas of Irvine and Grangemouth-Falkirk; certain older industrial areas (North Lanarkshire, Central Fife, the Vale of Leven and the part of the Lothians which forms the hinterland of Livingston). The first two groups are classed as *major* growth areas, while the older industrial districts are distinct in their reserves of industrial labour, their restricted possibilities for housing and rehousing, and their great need for clearance and rehabilitation. They are all in the one category of financial support, however, which is not to be limited to its local or immediate needs: 'in these growth areas . . . the wide range of financial inducements available to industry in development districts will be maintained until there is

*Broadsheets on Britain No. 14, H.M.S.O. 1964.

strong evidence of a general and sustained improvement in employment in Central Scotland as a whole'.*

The prime objectives, then, are clear:

1. To promote faster economic growth by reviving older industries, by introducing new, modern industries, and by modernising the complete infrastructure of industrial and social life in the region.

2. To avoid phases of industrial stagnation, and to provide steady, assured employment to the greatest number of workers, and thus to offset the migration of people from Scotland.

3. To improve living conditions by schemes of rehabilitation, by lessening overcrowding in Glasgow and its neighbourhood, and, by the creation of the new townships, to attract some of Glasgow's 'overspill' population.

With its many advantages, the Central Lowlands is a zone of great economic potential. For this reason, this programme of development is of extreme importance to the well-being of Scotland, and of Great Britain. It anticipates the social and industrial pattern of the future. Its measures point to a way of life and an economy which most of the people of Scotland will experience during the rest of this century, at least.

THREE NEW SCOTTISH INDUSTRIES

The Motor Vehicle Industry. There are three broad phases of development in the motor vehicle industry of Scotland. All pertain to the present century; each is of special interest and importance.

Scotland played a part in the pioneer stage of the industry in Great Britain. During the first twenty five years of the century, when many models were being tried out, factories in Glasgow, Paisley and Dumfries were in the field: Albion, Argyll, North British Motors, Arrol-Johnston, Galloway and Beardmore, were names familiar in the car industry of this period. The industry was short-lived in Scotland, however, for by the difficult years of the 1930s, none but the Albion plant had survived. (Today, Albion commercial trucks and buses are built at Scotstoun, Glasgow, and this factory is one of the

*Central Scotland, A Programme for Development and Growth, H.M.S.O. 1963.

most important producers of vehicles in Scotland.) For the rest, mass production, backed by the manufacture on a large scale of machine tools and components, had drawn the industry away from Scotland to the centres with superior locational advantages in the Midlands and South of England.

The second phase began in the years after the Second World War. In nearly every part of the world, as well as in our own land, the post-war years meant large-scale reconstruction and development. The age of the earth-moving vehicle had emerged; it was now possible to use giant-size vehicles for speedy digging, transferring, levelling and removing huge quantities of earth and rubble from sites, prior to the construction of large buildings, housing schemes, motorways, etc. In the manufacture of vehicles of this sort, Scotland has had a noteworthy share. In 1950, the first factory – Euclid – for making such vehicles was set up at Newhouse Industrial Estate. Six years later, the Caterpillar plant came into being at Tannochside, Uddingston. From the outset, both have been associated with parent establishments in America. The vehicles made by both plants are all in the heavy class – rubber tyred or tracked, of great tonnage, with a variety of attachments, front and rear, and sufficiently robust to stand up to the most exacting physical conditions. They are in use today on constructional sites all over Great Britain, but, above all, there is a substantial export market for them in every quarter of the globe. The output of the factories is such that Scotland is second only to America in the export of these vehicles. Together, the two concerns provide work for over 2,500 employees (some of the Euclid workers making gears at the branch factory at Peterhead). Steel for the industry is supplied by Clydeside steelworks, and components are drawn from nearby factories, e.g. in Shotts (engines), and in Hillington (tractor equipment). This branch of the vehicle industry is still young, but its growth in Scotland has been most impressive.

The third development is of very recent date. In 1961, a new B.M.C. factory at Bathgate started to produce commercial trucks and tractors. The factory is located on the main A8 road (Glasgow-Edinburgh), a situation which offers the distinct advantage of short distance and quick transport to the ports of Leith, Glasgow and Grangemouth. It is very near to the new town of Livingston, which is designed to house a large proportion of its workers. The weekly output of the factory is now 800 trucks and 400 tractors, and both these figures are expected to rise when the factory is in full production, with employment for 4,000 to 5,000 workers.

As late as 1963, another huge factory began production at Linwood, west of Paisley. An offshoot of the Rootes Group of the Midlands of England, this plant differs from the others described so far, in that it produces cars for the private owner, and is capable of producing them at the rate of 3,000 minicars per week. In an age when a motor car is within the reach of such a large proportion of society, this type of small car is not only very attractive on the home market, it is also very profitable as an export. From such a new activity, many other benefits to the economy emerge. At Linwood, across the road from the car factory, is the great Pressed Steel Company plant, which, relying on steel from the Gartcosh-Ravenscraig strip mills, provides the car bodies and bodies for the B.M.C. trucks. This plant also sends bodies and cabs to car manufacturing centres in England and in Sweden. Developments in the ancillary and component branches of the industry are also taking place. New factories have opened at Cumbernauld, Larkhall, Chapelhall and West Calder, and existing manufacturers of various car-making 'ingredients' have benefited by orders from Scotland's own assembly industry. Supporting manufactures, forming an industrial complex with the vehicle-building works at the core, are in fact essential to the growth and permanence of these larger and more recent developments, and they attract considerable Government assistance – as did the two main producers of vehicles at Bathgate and Linwood.

The motor vehicle industry is a good example of the new 'growth industries' of Scotland, not only because of its extensions into a wide range of engineering and other manufactures, and its large 'consumer market'; it also has its repercussions deep in the roots of traditional heavy industry. Hitherto, much steel was destined for the heavy engineering industries, especially constructional work and ship building. Nowadays, there is a great demand for strip and sheet steel, and a very large proportion of this is for the new branches of the vehicle industry. This radical reorientation of steel making is evidence of the vitality of motor manufacturing as a Scottish industry, and equally impressive is the redeployment of labour: several thousands of employees in the motor vehicle industry represent a major achievement in training, and a vital extension in new skills of twentieth century engineering.

The Oil and Petro-chemical Industry. Although the West Lothian shale-oil industry has now ceased production, Scotland is still strongly interested in the oil and oil-derived industries, both through the import of crude oil and the refining of petroleum. Oil refining

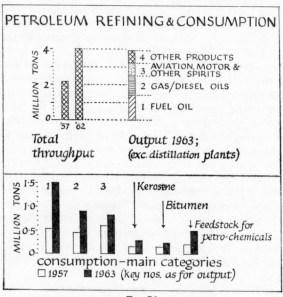

Fig. 76

increased by almost 90 per cent between 1957 and 1962. There are three small-size refining plants at Ardrossan (making bitumen for road surfaces), at Pumpherston (now using oil from small oilfields in England), and at Dundee (bitumen and tar distillation). But far more important than these is Grangemouth, the principal oil refining centre in Scotland. Its refinery, owned and operated by a large firm with refineries elsewhere in Great Britain, has experienced a high rate of growth in recent years. In 1954 its capacity was 2½ million tons; now, as a result of expansion, it is capable of handling 4½ million tons. The refinery produces petrol as well as liquid gas, diesel oil, paraffin and fuel oils. (Fig. 76 illustrates the relative importance of Scotland's refinery products.) The output of these spirits, oils and other petroleum products, most of which are so familiar and so vital in our modern society, are distributed throughout Scotland by road tankers, and tanker rail-wagons. Distribution also takes place from Grangemouth docks by coastal and deep sea tankers.

The petro-chemical industry, aptly named, is concerned with the synthesis, or combination, of carbon and other chemical elements derived from petroleum. It is dependent, to a large extent, on supplies of 'ready made' gases, obtained during the refining processes. The raw material is thus at hand, and there is a steady and ample flow from the refinery: as a feedstock it is the source of a great quantity and variety of chemicals; and these have revolutionised the chemical industry itself. Thus, Grangemouth is a fine example of rapid growth in a new, and technologically fertile industry of the twentieth century. From 1947 to 1963, no fewer than seven different petro-chemical plants have come into existence in Grangemouth. Such a chemical complex, as it is styled, prepares a great number of very special petro-chemicals as the 'intermediates' which have yet to undergo further processing before they become the finished products of many different types of factory. (These finished products have rarely much resemblance to petroleum itself.) Grangemouth is not yet a centre for the production of the finished goods; it is mainly concerned with the preparation of the intermediate petro-chemicals, and with their distribution to factories in Scotland and, even more so, in England and Wales. But the following list indicates the versatility of petro-chemicals, and helps to explain the immense scope for their expansion in the industrial pattern of Scotland, an expansion which provides fresh employment for technically trained workers.

Common examples of petro-chemicals prepared at Grangemouth are:

ethylene (for making anti-freeze mixtures, stimulants and fumigants for crops, anaesthetics);

propylene (for making industrial solvents and soil fumigants);

dodecyl benzene (useful in making grease-solvent and soapless detergents);

cumene/phenol (used in making resins, agricultural chemicals and drugs);

polyethylene (resins used in non-breaking containers, bottles, buckets etc. including articles for medical and laboratory use);
styrene monomer (plastic materials, paints and resins);
polybutadiene (basis of synthetic rubber for tyres etc.);
acrylonitrile (acrylic fibres used in clothing).

The Electronics Industry. The manufacture of electronic equipment is a further example of the growth of modern industry in Scotland, and one of the finest indications of development in a branch of engineering requiring the most advanced technology. The industry did not exist before the 1950s, but already there are over twenty firms in Scotland. It is still in its initial phase of development, yet the rate of growth has been undoubtedly significant in several respects. First, the industry is providing a new source of employment, estimated, at present, at 20,000, including a proportion of university graduates. In addition, more and more factory space is being occupied in Central Scotland where its products can be of benefit to a wide range of other industries, and some of this is located, aptly enough, in the New Towns. Noteworthy too, is the fact that the firms are not wholly of Scottish origin; some are English and American firms which have been sufficiently attracted to Scotland to establish offshoots here. Then, within the last decade, the application of electronic techniques has become increasingly valuable in the Scottish industrial and commercial world.

In Scotland, this industry concentrates on industrial products, of wide range and of a highly technical character, and the factories are widely dispersed in the Central Lowlands. One principal factory is situated in Edinburgh, with offshoots in Dundee and Dalkeith. It turns out such modern products as miniature electrical circuits, compact and reliable, for use in computers, air navigation devices, control systems for machine tools and equipment for detecting faults in power lines. The following are further examples of the range of products and, though the list is not complete, it illustrates the many services provided by electronics to other engineering industries, to many aspects of transport and communications, and, through a range of factory processes, to the everyday life of the citizen:

Newhouse Industrial Estate: computers with electronic data processing; heating and ventilating systems; hospital apparatus.

Spango Valley, Greenock: punch-card and accounting machines; time and data processing systems; automatic typewriters.

Cumbernauld and Dundee: accounting and calculating office machinery.

East Kilbride: equipment for missile guidance systems; controls for domestic appliances.

Glenrothes: oxygen analysers; precision potentiometers; meters for measuring alkalinity of liquids.

Aberdeen and Pittenweem: assembly of sea-radio and echometer appliances.

Airdrie: hearing aids.

Penicuik: thermostatic equipment (including detection device for road frost).

Galashiels: printed circuits for many other Scottish and English electronics factories.

Wishaw, Hillington and Carfin: time switches; high speed receivers; ultrasonic flaw detectors.

Busby: smoke density meters for fish curing kilns.

Glasgow: micro-testing and recording apparatus (medical and industrial) data scanning and logging apparatus (for calculating and control equipment); precision optical instruments.

These products of a young industry, none of them made even twenty years ago, are vastly different from Scotland's traditional products. By their accuracy and their capacity to save time and labour, an amazing transformation has been brought about in our industrial and commercial life. The result of thorough and constant research, the miracles of automation and electronic computation are becoming more and more an essential feature of the modern world. But not only are Scottish-made electronic products invaluable to us at home, they find a ready sale abroad, and strengthen our export potential in value and diversity. Electronics is thus one of the most vigorous of the so-called growth industries.

THREE MAJOR TRENDS IN ECONOMIC DEVELOPMENT

Having considered three modern industrial enterprises, some of the broader trends in development in the Central Lowlands must be noted. Three of these trends are: changes of employment structure;

16

changes in the infrastructure (power, communications and public services generally); changes in the distribution of population and settlement.

Employment structure

Major changes here are shown by Fig. 77 and the notes attached, and factors involved in these changes, such as the diversification of industry, have been referred to elsewhere. But it is also worth remembering the rôle which automation plays increasingly in the structure of industrial and commercial employment. The applications of electronics to manufacturing processes reduce the labour force required in some industries more readily than in others. In fact, numbers employed is less than ever a useful measure of an industry as a productive segment of the whole economy. The highly valued expansion of the chemical and oil-refining industry in Scotland has been accomplished with an actual reduction of the total labour force. Automation has been highly successful here, as it has been in the modern extension of Scottish steel furnace and mill capacity, in coal mining, and in all the fields of energy production.

Many industries (e.g. the assembly industries of shipbuilding and vehicle manufacture) have yet to reach the level of automation attained by some competitors abroad, and the stimulus of American-based firms operating in Scotland is all the more important where they bring experience of automation with them. The eventual

FIG. 77

Note:

1. There has been a general fall in employment in all primary industries.
2. Of the primary industries, fishermen (including crofter-fishermen) in the crofting counties, farm and forestry workers in the remainder of northern Scotland, and miners in the west-central region have decreased most notably.
3. Taking the three main groups of manufacturing together, there has been a considerable increase in employment, the region gaining most in this respect being the west-central region, and the largest gains being in the metal making and engineering industries.
4. While textiles maintained their position in the crofting counties, and increased in importance in the southern region, for Scotland as a whole the fall in employment was very decided.
5. While all regions show new employment in the food, drink and tobacco industries, and the biggest absolute gain in this category is seen in the west-central region, both northern regions exceeded the rest of Scotland in relative terms.
6. The general decline in employment in transport and communications is proportionately highest in the south and north, except for the crofting counties.

(A) REGIONAL STRUCTURE OF EMPLOYMENT (OCCUPATIONS) & CHANGES 1951-1961 (Based on estimates for 1961)

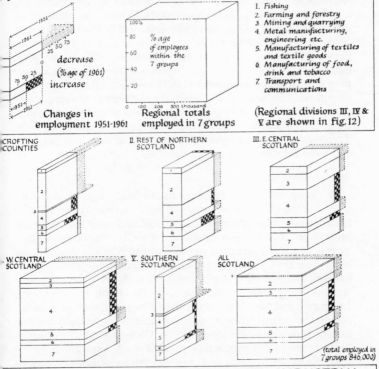

Key:

decrease (%age of 1961) increase

Changes in employment 1951-1961

% age of employees within the 7 groups

Regional totals employed in 7 groups

Seven main occupation groups:
1. Fishing
2. Farming and forestry
3. Mining and quarrying
4. Metal manufacturing, engineering etc.
5. Manufacturing of textiles and textile goods
6. Manufacturing of food, drink and tobacco
7. Transport and communications

(Regional divisions III, IV & V are shown in fig. 12)

I. CROFTING COUNTIES

II. REST OF NORTHERN SCOTLAND

III. E. CENTRAL SCOTLAND

IV. W. CENTRAL SCOTLAND

V. SOUTHERN SCOTLAND

ALL SCOTLAND (total employed in 7 groups 846,000)

(B) EMPLOYMENT ARISING FROM NEW INDUSTRIAL BUILDING IN MANUFACTURING INDUSTRIES

1 2 3 4 5 6 7 8 9 10 11 12 13 14 15 16 17 18 thousands

Engineering and electrical goods

Vehicles

Clothing and footwear

Food, drink and tobacco

Textiles

Bricks, pottery, glass, cement etc.

Metal manufacture

Paper, printing and publishing

Timber, furniture, etc.

Metal goods not specified elsewhere

Chemicals and allied industries

Key: (Building categories) ▨ 1960-June 1964 inclusive ☐ Under construction at June 1964

FIG 77

pattern of employment in the second half of the twentieth century will depend largely on the rate of investment in new machinery, and the training of workers in new skills. In turn, the attraction of capital and highly trained men and women will be toward areas well served by the infrastructure now being planned, and thus new regional patterns of settlement and population will emerge. One example of these interdependent factors is seen in the present planning of a large new electronics factory at South Queensferry, after careful consideration of site factors by the parent American company. High priority in this consideration was given to communications, both by rail and road bridge over the Forth and by air from Turnhouse, and to the nearby resources of Edinburgh for scientific and technical staff and research facilities.

The Infrastructure

(i) **Power and Water Supplies.** In the vital topic of electricity supply in the Central Lowlands it is only necessary to recall what has already been described in Chapter VIII, and point to some future possibilities. But the generation of power is distinct from other aspects of the infrastructure in the extent to which it also operates above this level, functioning itself as an industry, consuming raw material and providing employment. Thus the new thermal-power stations being built on the shores of the Forth (at Cockenzie, Longannet and Methil) are more than a means of increasing power supplies in the east: they are an investment in the future of the coal mining industry in the region. The Cockenzie plant – which is likely to be in full production by 1968 – will burn about 10,000 tons of coal daily, while at Longannet the huge supplies required appear to justify the planning of underground transport from mine to power station. In all, about a quarter of the total output of coal sold in Scotland is already used in the generation of electricity, and of the total electricity produced by all methods of generation, some 40 per cent is used by industry.

It should also be remembered that, for a shorter duration, the new power-stations stimulate many branches of the Scottish engineering industry. An example of this is seen in the provision of boilers, and associated equipment, for Longannet, which will occupy Clydebank and Dumbarton firms in the largest undertaking they have ever had, and will take six or seven years to fulfil.

Returning to the generation of electric power as a part of the industrial infrastructure, there are other generating projects beyond those on the Firth of Forth. At Hunterston, the world's largest nuclear generating station has brought Scotland to the leading place in the world for consumption, per head of population, of nuclear electricity. Yet this alone will not be sufficient power for the needs of the west Central Lowlands, and another large thermal station is forecast for the region – perhaps to be sited in the growth area of Irvine, and probably burning oil rather than coal. Supplementary power for peak-load use will also be needed, and the North of Scotland's hydro-electricity will almost certainly be used for this purpose on a greater scale than ever before. The pumped-storage scheme at Ben Cruachan* may well be repeated elsewhere, and the adaptation of Loch Sloy Hydro-Electric Power scheme for this purpose has been suggested, an adaptation which would increase its value to the Central Lowlands very considerably.

While electricity as a source of industrial power has made more obvious strides forward, a more recent, and perhaps less well known feature of Scotland's progress has been that of the gas industry. Reference has been made already to the Lurgi high-pressure gas plant operated at Westfield in Fife, but more recent still, and more significant for the future has been the installation of oil-based gas making plant. Using light petroleum distillate, the industry has achieved a 'breakthrough', research in the 'reforming' processes applied to the feedstock having enabled this most economic of raw materials to replace the more expensive traditional fuel – coal. The largest of these new plants, at Provan (Glasgow) will have a capacity, by the end of 1965, larger than the present total production from all Scottish gasworks. A smaller distillate plant is also being built at Kilmarnock, but the value of these new works will be more than locally beneficial: the new super-grid, begun in 1958, will give the gas industry a new flexibility and range in its supply throughout the Central Lowlands, and beyond. We are more familiar with high-power electricity transmission, through its visible evidence in the

*The Cruachan scheme is dual-purpose. By day, water from a high-level reservoir is harnessed to underground generators (in the heart of the mountain) which produce electricity at peak periods. The water then discharges into Loch Awe from which, overnight, electric pumps lift it back again to the high-level reservoir for later use.

landscape, but the underground gas mains could be very significant too for industry in the future. Important new projects in the steel, aluminium and motor-vehicle industries have been initiated on the basis of this fuel, and the super-grid (operating at high pressure first

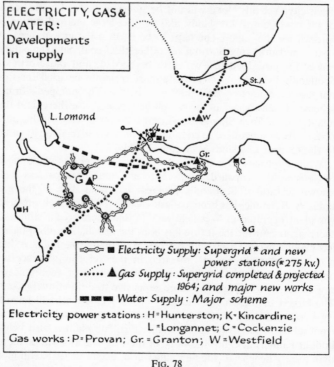

ELECTRICITY, GAS & WATER: Developments in supply

=o=o= ■ *Electricity Supply: Supergrid * and new power stations (* 275 kv.)*

······ ▲ *Gas Supply: Supergrid completed & projected 1964; and major new works*

■■ ■■ ■■ *Water Supply: Major scheme*

Electricity power stations: H = Hunterston; K = Kincardine; L = Longannet; C = Cockenzie

Gas works: P = Provan; Gr. = Granton; W = Westfield

FIG. 78

made feasible by the Lurgi plant) will play a vital part in widening industrial applications of gas. Finally, in this summary of a resurgent industry, there are exciting, if unknown, possibilities in the present surveys of the North Sea for oil and/or natural gas: explorations in which the gas industry has a strong stake.

The general significance of water supply has been emphasised already (see Chapter IX), but, in a phase of expansion and reorganisation, it is clear that this essential component in the infra-structure must be provided in a carefully planned programme. The siting of the atomic power-station at Hunterston, and of the new thermal power-stations on the banks of the Forth, are examples of the continued importance of water as a locational factor in some industrial sitings. But, apart from coastal access to sea water for cooling purposes, industry must be given more freedom from the restraints of older water-based sites, where each factory catered for its own needs, and equally from the restrictions of mains supplies derived from smaller authorities which are unable to cope, separately, with increased demands. New urban areas make their own claims for domestic supplies, and these too call for wider planning of resources. The new Loch Lomond water supply project will cater for five growth areas (see Fig. 78) while the three major cities are all engaged in assuring adequate future reserves, Glasgow from Glenfinlas, Edinburgh from the Fruid reservoir, and Dundee from the Back Water Reservoir. Plans to meet needs in other areas, e.g. Fife and Ayrshire, are now being made, and regional all-purpose water-boards are being formed to carry through these schemes and ensure that new industries and housing areas are adequately serviced.

(ii) **Communications of the Future.** Physical geography has always been a major obstacle to communications in Central Scotland. The long firths, penetrating far inland, both east and west, rendered some form of man-made crossing imperative from very early times. The opening of the Clyde tunnel and the inauguration of the Forth Road Bridge were signal events of mid-twentieth century engineer-ing. In this modern age, structural achievements such as these exemplify long-term economic strategy. An expanding economy is sustained by an efficient system of communications. Thus, in the programme of development high priority is accorded to it, and substantial sums are available from the Exchequer for the provision of new and improved means of transport.

Roads. The process of reconstruction will be speeded up to provide a regional network beneficial to expanding industries and growth areas. Within the next few years, the following stages of modernisa-tion will be completed:

1. Reconstruction and extension of motorways or dual carriage-ways, especially along A8 (Glasgow–Edinburgh and Glasgow–Greenock), A80 (Glasgow–Stirling), A9 (Edinburgh–Perth, including

by-passes for Falkirk and Stirling), A90 (Inverkeithing–Perth, by-passing Cowdenbeath and Kelty), A74 (Glasgow–Carlisle). The last, A74, is the most important commercial highway of Scotland, linking Clydeside to the English motorway system, and the largest single trunk road project.

2. More localised, but extremely vital, road improvements will be implemented by bridge, diversion and by-pass. The Tay Road Bridge, the bridging of the Clyde at Erskine, and a new bridge over the River Leven north of Dumbarton (part of the Alexandria by-pass) are notable among these schemes, but also of immense benefit to the future integration of communications are the improvements planned for access to the airports of Abbotsinch, Turnhouse and Prestwick.

Further in the future, but undoubtedly necessary for the eventual progress of industry in the Central Lowlands, is the plan for a major east-west motorway which would link the growth area of the Lothians, centred on Livingston, with that of Irvine to the west and the port of Leith in the east.

Airports. Apart from the problem of access by road, mentioned above, facilities are to be improved in terminal buildings and run-ways. Over the last five years, the number of passengers using Scotland's airports has more than doubled, while freight carried has increased two and a half times. A recent strengthening of the international status of Prestwick has been the decision to run a daily service to New York, all the year round, and there have been improvements in the services connecting Glasgow and Edinburgh to cities in England. More difficult has been the effective connection of Dundee to the internal air network, but a landing strip there has been completed and small aircraft operate a service to Edinburgh.

Ports. In the light of the needs of both older and newer industries, development proposals have been framed for the ports of the Clyde and the Forth. At Glasgow, the modernisation of Prince's Dock and extension of the large Meadowside granary (by some 70 per cent of existing storage capacity) indicate the present efforts to meet demands for handling the trade of the port more efficiently. But longer-term needs, for ore carriers and oil tankers for instance, require deeper water above Greenock, and new terminal installa-tions. It has been increasingly realised that the future of the port of

Glasgow depends on improvements throughout the whole of the navigable stretch of the Clyde, and that a unified authority must be formed to carry out such developments. While shipping using west coast ports has decreased in tonnage from 63 to 58 per cent of Scotland's total over the last five years, much of the corresponding increase on the east coast can be attributed to industrial activity in the east Central Lowlands. Apart from plans to unify port authority for the Forth, as for the Clyde, a major step towards modernisation has already been taken there, with agreement reached on the Leith Dock development scheme, to be completed in 1968. This will create a deep-water port for the Central Lowlands on its eastern seaboard, able to accommodate large oil-tankers, tourist vessels, and general cargo ships of a much larger tonnage than at present.

Railways. Here too, modern transport services must be geared to the expanding economy, and while rationalisation of the whole of Scotland's railway network is called for, as part of the plan based on the 'Beeching Report', in the Central Lowlands this is 'unlikely to have any widespread serious impact'* on passenger lines. Within recent years, in fact, the passenger services in the region have been vastly modernised by electric and diesel services, e.g. the 'Blue Trains' serving suburban communities in and around Glasgow, and the frequent one-hour diesel link between Glasgow and Edinburgh. Modern freight services are already serving industry with adaptations to many of the developments which call for special facilities e.g. express car-transportation from Linwood to England, express, high-capacity tank cars from South Wales to the new Provan gas works, and, from the new cement works at Dunbar (which will eventually cater for a demand equal to a third of Scotland's present needs). Other specialised tankers will connect with main distribution depots in the east Central Lowlands.

Changes in the Distribution of Population and Settlement

The developments described above are, inevitably, re-orienting the pattern of settlement and population in the Central Lowlands. Changes in man-power requirements, brought about by more varied industry, and by automation, demand greater mobility in

Central Scotland, A Programme for Development and Growth, H.M.S.O. 1963.

employment, and thus some loosening of the hold of existing concentrations of population. Similarly, the wider distribution of power, transport, and other services; the freedom from an earlier coalfield and waterside complex of locations; and, most important, the deliberate planning for better urban life – at present made difficult by the congestion of housing and of traffic: all these factors operate in reducing the magnetism of existing conurbations, and especially in reducing the polarity of Clyde and Forth.

Glasgow and the Clyde will continue to dominate the population distribution in the Central Lowlands, however. During the ten years, 1951 to 1961, when East Kilbride grew from 5,000 to 32,000, Glasgow lost 35,000 people; but this is a loss of only 3 per cent of Glasgow's total population, and even the accelerated planning of the growth areas now envisages a total of little more than 300,000 by 1981, or perhaps a half-million in population eventually, i.e. 8 to 11 per cent of Central Scotland's present population.

The most balanced view of the future gained from such considerations is that there will be an interlacing of the older – still dominant – settlements with the newer urban areas, and some of the sharper population contrasts of today will become less abrupt. New beads will be strung, so to speak, along the population necklace of the Central Lowlands. In this way the east-west contrasts may become less obvious. Though never clearly separated in the Falkirk-Stirling area, the Clyde and Forth basins have been distinct units in the settlement pattern of the past; but now the growth areas are to develop astride the central 'watershed' of population. The growth area centred on Cumbernauld will be separated by a mere mile or two from that of Falkirk-Grangemouth, and that of North Lanarkshire less than 10 miles from the Livingston growth area.

It may be that the bridging of the east-west structure of population clusters will be accompanied by a more balanced distribution between these two sides of the Central Lowlands. In the intercensal years (1951-61), however, this has not become apparent. While Glasgow lost 3 per cent and Dundee gained 3 per cent, Edinburgh remained virtually unchanged in population, and the eastern area as a whole gained less than half as many people as the west. The only features of population change which remain to be noted therefore are those which are, for reasons of size and clarity, most easily discerned: the New Towns, and the redeveloped city of Glasgow.

The New Towns. All towns have origins of some sort. The circumstances of their birth may be obscure, and may not be traced easily or with great exactitude. Some Scottish towns took shape in the distant past, and reached their present size and functions through a gradual, haphazard evolution. With the advent of the Industrial Revolution, many towns sprang to life in the Central Lowlands. Through the intervening years their functions have, in many instances, changed but little: they remain centres of industry, and have grown to a maturity in indeterminate fashion – ill-planned, insanitary and congested.

Now, at last, a bold step is being taken to be rid of glaring urban overcrowding and disarray. For the first time in Central Scotland, a full programme for New Towns is in operation. Four New Towns have been deliberately planned, and are being actively created. The first, East Kilbride, came into existence as early as 1947, while Cumbernauld is a creation of recent years. Both have been built to relieve the pressure of population in Glasgow, and are close to that city. In Fife, Glenrothes, developed in the 1950s, is a new town which is also taking overspill population from Glasgow. On a site near Bathgate, and not far from Edinburgh, Livingston is the latest town to take shape in Scotland. It is a creation of the middle 1960s. Finally, and most recently, a technical survey has established the practicability of developing yet another New Town in Irvine. The New Towns, and many other older towns all over Scotland, have overspill agreements with Glasgow.

The New Towns are, and will be, of the most modern style and lay-out. They are set in attractively fresh and spacious surroundings, and each has evolved distinctive systems of roads and pedestrian ways. Shopping centres, houses, cultural and religious buildings, all illustrate contemporary design and the use of modern materials. Each accepts the age of the motor vehicle, catering for public parking and private garaging.

But these New Towns are not intended solely as reception areas for the rehabilitation of people from Glasgow. There is another vital reason for their existence: they are industrial growth points. Their industries, gaining strength as the towns grow, are creating a new and modern complex of activity across the Forth and Clyde basins.

East Kilbride, its population now about 40,000 (estimated 1964), has experienced a remarkable phase of industrial growth since its inception. Over 60 different firms occupy more than two million square feet of factory space in what was virtually a country village not long ago. At first, Glenrothes was to be a major coal mining centre in Fife. This did not materialise however, and it is now a modern township of 16,000 (est. 1964) with about a score of firms established there. Cumbernauld (11,500) (est. 1964) with easy access to Grangemouth, Glasgow and Edinburgh, now has fifteen different factories, covering about three-quarters of a million square feet, and more have planned to come. Livingston, still in its infancy, provides many houses for workers in the B.M.C. vehicle factory at Bathgate, and its master plan aims at the provision of extensive industrial building, some already taking shape.

Both for the economy of Scotland, and for the welfare of its people, new townships such as these are beneficial, and, indeed, vital. The programme of town planning and development exemplifies one of the major aspects of change current in Central Scotland.

Glasgow: a City of Change. The New Towns have the twofold objective of housing Glasgow's overspill population and of creating a new source of industrial activity in Central Scotland. Within the city of Glasgow, however, a programme of renovation and modernisation is also taking place. The City's Development Plan* is a comprehensive one, embracing many aspects of urban life and extending over the remaining decades of the century. Foremost in this plan are the following items:

1. *The rehabilitation and redistribution* of thousands of Glasgow's citizens. Between the wars, overcrowding in the city was partly met by building large, suburban housing estates, consisting of two and three storey buildings. Now, multi-storey flats create an entirely new urban landscape in every quarter of Glasgow. The ultimate aim is the elimination of the unsavoury slum areas.

2. *The improvement of Glasgow's communications.* From a very thorough survey† has emerged a vast and far-looking scheme for the modernisation and development of Glasgow's communications, e.g. in the creation of an inner ring road, with new river crossings, adequate for the increased road traffic of the future.

*The Survey Report of the City of Glasgow Development Plan. Quinquennial Review, 1960.

†Interim Report on the Glasgow Inner Ring Road, 1962.

3. *The creation of development areas.* These are to be seven in number, and, in addition to residential improvements, there are to be cultural, commercial and industrial developments. The new buildings in the central part of the city will include those of the new University of Strathclyde, and other colleges. Already these buildings have made a striking transformation in the Glasgow skyline.

Glasgow is earnestly engaged in this formidable plan: a campaign of renovation worked out with great deliberation by a team of town planners. No one can refute that the project of reconstruction is an urgent one; and no one can deny the expectation of a new Glasgow, arising from the plan: new in physical appearance, and a challenge to the resolution and vigour of its people.

DEVELOPMENTS IN SCOTTISH AGRICULTURE

While the broad pattern of farming in Scotland has remained generally constant, and regional variations are still adequately represented by Fig. 14, there have been some notable changes in emphasis in the post-war years.

Increases of output as a whole (14 per cent over the last ten years) are the result of improvement in techniques in farming, improved varieties of seed, and breeds of cattle and sheep, the wider use of fertilisers and of chemical control of weeds and pests; but also the result of economic conditions too – the high level of consumption of Scottish farm produce in Britain, and the support of agriculture by government (in subsidies, deficiency payments, etc.).

The relative importance of particular livestock and crop interests are also affected by these factors, since they all have some selective effect in stimulating the farming economy. Thus, widespread mechanisation, and a diminishing labour force, favour cereals rather than root crops, and amongst the latter potatoes are at a disadvantage compared with sugar beet.

Reference to the accompanying diagrams will show some of the following trends for the period 1953 to 1962, but two facts should be borne in mind: the trends are largely a continuation of longer-term post-war changes, and many are true for Britain as a whole (e.g. declining tillage, rising areas of rotation grass, increases in barley over other cereals).

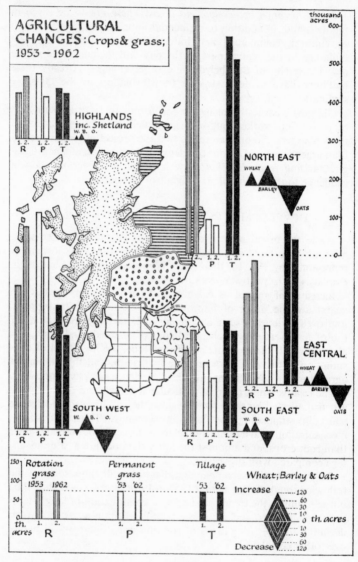

AGRICULTURAL CHANGES: Crops & grass; 1953 – 1962

Fig. 79

1. The dominance of livestock interests in Scottish farming has been more than maintained, the value of output having risen more than that of crops.

2. While the total area of crops and grass has not greatly changed, both permanent grass and tillage have lost ground to rotation grass. Increased yield per acre of almost all crops, and the better quality of permanent grassland, compensate for the loss of acreage and the value of all crops has risen quite significantly.

3. The west of Scotland, and in particular the South West, shows greater losses in areas of permanent grass and tillage, and correspondingly greater increases in rotation grass acreage, than the eastern regions, and this must be closely related to the relative importance of turnips and oats in the cropping regime of the west, and to changes in livestock feeding.

4. The very considerable decline in the oats crop and the rise of barley, and to a lesser extent wheat, acreages can be accounted for partly by the better varieties of barley available for northern and western climates (and the suitability of these new varieties for combine-harvesting), and partly to the more intensive feeding policy – especially in beef production. Though smaller in total areas, the increases of barley in the western regions are most striking, (1962 acreage being more than eight times that of 1953 in the south west).

5. Root crops have lost ground more than cereals, and here the turnip and swede acreages have decreased most of all, followed by those of the main crop and second-early potatoes. The increased yield (two tons per acre in the last ten years) does not compensate for the decrease in acreage, and production has fallen by 10 per cent.

6. While the number of cattle as a whole has shown a considerable rise, the increase has been in fact restricted to beef cattle. Dairy cattle have been reduced numerically, although higher yields per cow have given a larger total output of milk. The marked rise in the numbers of beef cattle is most notable in animals under two years old (80 per cent more than 10 years ago): a reflection on the trend to more intensive feeding of young cattle to meet present day food preferences.

7. While numbers of sheep have increased, those of pigs and poultry have decreased. One regional change of emphasis is in the

relative importance today of south and central Scotland for poultry. This follows from the development of the broiler-fowl industry and larger numbers of turkeys being raised in southern Scotland.

LAND USE IN THE HIGHLANDS AND ISLANDS

Changes in the economy of the Highlands and Islands are less easily summarised than those of the Central Lowlands, for while the developments in the latter region are massive and manifold, they are also in many respects a coherent outcome of past pressures and present planning. On the other hand the Highlands have shown the fragmentation of a region in retreat; the diversity of decay. It is too soon to detect more than isolated areas of economic vigour, and tentative trends toward general recovery. It is all the more unwise to predict the future of the region since the government initiative in 1965 in forming a Highland Development Board may lead to faster rates of change, new directions of economic deployment, and areas of growth not yet considered. It is for this reason that we are concerned here with one item only in the Highland economy, and that item the one which has a clearly discernible pattern, if an uncertain future.

A recent Report of the Advisory Panel on the Highlands and Islands.* provides data on which to assess the present state of land use (see Figs. 80-81). It also discusses the problems which arise and makes practical proposals for improvements in usage under four headings: agriculture, forestry, sport and physical recreation (including tourism), and industrial and 'urban' uses.

The agricultural problems of the region remain those described in Chapter XVI: marginal land deteriorating where an unbalanced grazing of sheep predominates; lack of winter keep, and of finance for the improvement of land by liming, bracken control, reseeding and other reclamation work. The Report does refer to a large amount of reclamation being carried out, e.g. in Lewis, but proposes more substantial schemes should be carried out by group co-operation, e.g. in the use of large machinery. But, more radically, there is also a demand in the Report for government to acquire land which is falling into decay and allow efficient farmers to develop and

*Land Use in the Highlands and Islands: Department of Agriculture and Fisheries for Scotland. H.M.S.O. 1964.

reclaim it. Reclamation, and land settlement in medium sized family farms are the two measures most clearly required in the future.

In crofting townships too, the Report recommends that more reorganisation of holdings, and the intake of non-crofting land should, where conditions are suitable, make for better economic

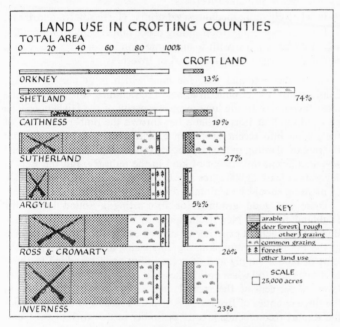

FIG. 80

units. The aim, it is thought, should be to strengthen the medium sized crofts, since very small crofts are not regarded as having a viable future in agricultural terms, while the large crofts, on the other hand, are already economic units giving full-time employment. The very small crofts are seen as a different challenge: one to be met less by land-use reform than by provision of other employment.

One should study therefore the regional distribution of crofts in

17

area-categories (Fig. 81) and note the pattern as one of potential improvement:

1. many small crofts; very few large ones: Lewis and west mainland of Ross-shire;
2. relatively more large crofts: Orkney; Caithness; east mainland of Ross-shire and Inverness;
3. relatively more medium sized crofts: Harris; Barra and Uists;
4. an average range (descending order numerically from smallest to medium size with a moderate number of larger acreage): Skye; Argyll; west mainland of Inverness.

Of all the potential uses for land which is at present under-employed or uneconomic in terms of agriculture, forestry is the one most favourable to the long-term prosperity of the Highlands. The new pulp-mill at Fort William has thrown the timber resources of the region into recent prominence, and it might be thought that the rate of planting in the last decade (about 14,000 acres each year) was a sufficient investment of land in the industry. But the Report suggests at least 23,000 acres a year can be justified, and such a rate of planting should be maintained for many years to come.

There are good grounds for forecasting a sound future for Highland forestry. New techniques, as well as new species, have shown the benefit of experiments carried out by the Research Branch of the Forestry Commission, e.g. in spacing and in pruning. Problems of labour supply and of accessibility must be added to those of climate and soil when noting the areas of forest at present (Fig. 80). Over 90 per cent of the area planted in the crofting counties is in the three counties of Inverness, Argyll and Ross and Cromarty, but the Report recommends greater flexibility in the work of the Commission: in areas chosen, the use of smaller blocks of land and in the policy of acquisition (e.g. in the crofting areas where the need is one of social and economic rehabilitation).

While some authorities have emphasised the rôle of forestry in a revitalised economy for the Highlands, others would give priority to tourism, and recreational purposes in general, as the most valuable single function for the region. It would seem best to regard neither of these modes of land-use as a panacea, and to consider both as essentially complementary to farming and crofting. The success of the Glenmore area in attracting visitors in both summer and winter

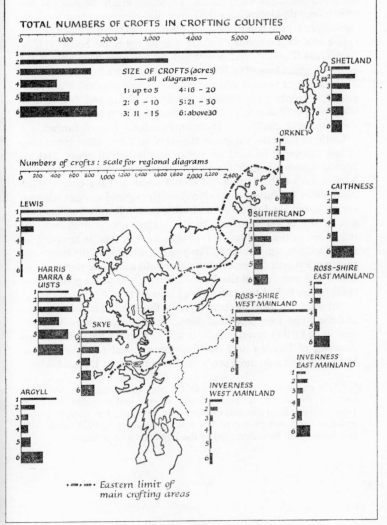

CROFTING COUNTIES: SIZE OF CROFTS 1964
(acreages excluding common grazing)

TOTAL NUMBERS OF CROFTS IN CROFTING COUNTIES

0   1,000   2,000   3,000   4,000   5,000   6,000

SIZE OF CROFTS (acres)
— all diagrams —

1: up to 5   4: 16 – 20
2: 6 – 10   5: 21 – 30
3: 11 – 15   6: above 30

Numbers of crofts : scale for regional diagrams

0   200   400   600   800   1,000   1,200   1,400   1,600   1,800   2,000   2,200   2,400

SHETLAND

ORKNEY

CAITHNESS

LEWIS

SUTHERLAND

HARRIS
BARRA &
UISTS

ROSS-SHIRE
EAST MAINLAND

ROSS-SHIRE
WEST MAINLAND

SKYE

INVERNESS
EAST MAINLAND

ARGYLL

INVERNESS
WEST MAINLAND

•—•—•—• Eastern limit of
main crofting areas

FIG. 81

– highlighted by the building of a large hotel near Aviemore – derives from the advantage of better facilities (e.g. ski-lifts) being offered to the tourist, and the Cairngorms as a whole are to be planned for recreational development in the future. But more dispersed facilities for visitors are not being neglected. Crofters are being assisted in providing chalets for holiday makers, tourist roads are being built in Argyll and Shetland, and new vehicle ferries have been introduced to the Western Isles. The Report suggests a closer link between the modern tourist interest and the older, but more exclusive, sporting estates, expanding the facilities for deer stalking and fishing to a wider public. Similarly, facilities for pony trekking and other recreational interests could, it is thought, be extended much further.

Lastly in this brief survey of Highland land use, there is the provision and siting of land for urban and industrial needs. Hydroelectric schemes, which have now, directly or indirectly, affected large areas of the Highlands, would seem to have only limited possibilities for future expansion (though pumped-storage schemes are projected for Loch Sloy and other areas). Rather than increase greatly the power resources of the region, efforts must now be redoubled in the attempt to find sites for factories as tempting in other facilities, e.g. transport. The possible selection of the Inverness-Invergordon area for new industrial growth should be noted as one that would make use of the most northerly point where general port facilities are linked to road and rail transport.*

But whatever local success may arise through industrial venture – and the Report suggests that natural resources, such as minerals, should be further investigated – it will be through the well adjusted blending of farming and crofting, forestry and tourism that the Highlands will gain most profit in the future use of the land.

*This area is to be linked also to the one new source of power forecast for the far north. Hitherto, the atomic energy establishment at Dounreay has been engaged on long-term research, but now it is proposed to site a new prototype fast reactor there, and by 1971 power from this reactor will be transmitted to the Highland grid at Beauly.

A NOTE ON
THE SCOTTISH ECONOMY, 1965-1970:
*A PLAN FOR EXPANSION**

The Plan aims to reduce emigration, and to use labour reserves more fully, by creating new jobs: 50-60,000 additional jobs, and 70-80,000 to replace losses in older industries. Government assistance will be increasingly available to workers changing

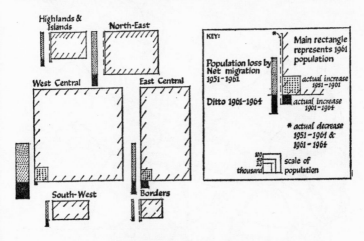

FIG. 82 Population changes by regions. Actual increase and net migration relative to 1961 population.

employment, in retraining, housing, and in direct financial help, while industry itself will gain grants and loans to encourage expansion in the Development Areas (now almost the whole of Scotland). Special efforts will be made to foster technological progress.

*Published for the Scottish Office, H.M.S.O., 1966

Agriculture is expected to develop in selective sectors, with increasing productivity and the release of many workers, and State forests will gain new plantings where these are most vital for the economy. The expansion of service industries, including tourism, will play an important part in the overall programme.

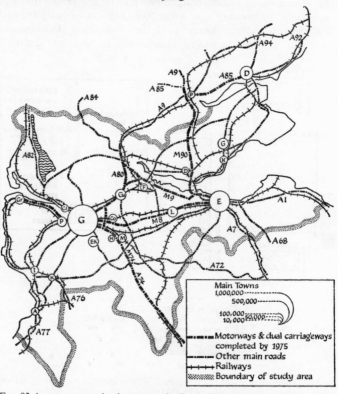

FIG. 83 A new communication system in Central Scotland. By 1970 the major concentrations of population will be closely knit together.

This recent Plan for Expansion goes further than previous Government reports in relating the major enterprise needed in the Central Lowlands to a balanced development in the rest of Scotland. Furthermore, the programme is a part of the National Plan for the whole of Britain's economy. Scotland's need is greater than that of most of the country: a need for faster rates of growth and higher rates of productivity to compensate for declining sectors of industry, and to stem the loss of young workers.

The following short account summarises the main prospects for the four 'Study Areas'. Central Scotland is thus not dealt with in this note, though naturally of major concern in the Plan itself, since the essential trends of the region have been treated already (pp. 222-245), and were envisaged, very largely, in the earlier *Programme for Development and Growth*.

The Borders (the Tweed basin with Liddesdale and Eskdale)

The Border counties have suffered acutely from prolonged depopulation. In the widely dispersed communities of the lower Tweed valley, improved farming methods have encouraged this outward movement, and here Berwick-upon-Tweed is the only town large enough to attract people and industry, and to be the economic pulse of the area. Berwick's potential for growth is seen to lie in accessibility (the main land routes could be augmented by fuller use of the harbour), and in the space available for new building. Thus it may draw in new industry, strengthen its hold on population and labour force, and further its role as a route centre.

In the western area, depopulation is also a problem. The cluster of textile centres relies largely on female labour, with few jobs for men, and apart from textiles there is little employment for men or women. The steady decline in the overall population, and the restricted scope for employment are drawbacks to industrial advancement. Alleviation may emerge through a deliberate programme of house building, and through the introduction of new industry, both in conjunction with an influx of newcomers. Implicit in such developments is the growth of a strong regional centre, increasing in population (25,000 within 10-15 years), in labour force, and in industrial diversity. Galashiels is selected as the town which possesses the locational advantages to expand rapidly into such a centre of economic and social influence.

South West Scotland (Galloway, Dumfriesshire and part of Ayrshire)

In this essentially rural area, farming is supported by no single dominant industry, as in the Borders, and though depopulation is

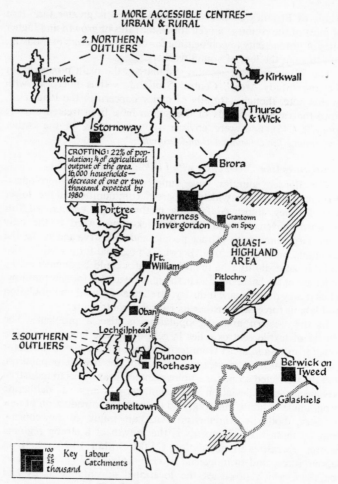

FIG. 84 FOUR REGIONAL STUDIES

Highland and Islands: decline in population and employment; fragmented settlements. Note the Thurso-Oban central axis of Highland-mainland (where urban growth has created 'holding area'). Bases for future development are marked 1, 2 and 3.

North-East: (1) Aberdeen area (51 per cent of population). Substantial decline

[*continued at foot of p. 257*

especially severe in Galloway it is mitigated in the region as a whole by a high rate of natural increase, and in south Ayrshire by some inward migration to the mining areas. Some larger service towns and forestry villages are stable centres of population, and in the Dumfries-Annan area there is some growth. Manufacturing industries, though small, are varied, and they are vital to the survival of the smaller market towns along the Solway lowlands. Stranraer, already important as a port, market and service centre, is referred to as a possible growth point in which investment should be concentrated. The Plan also points, most expectantly, to possible urban developments in the Lockerbie-Dumfries-Annan-Carlisle triangle. Annan already functions as a market centre with some industry (including the Chapelcross plant). Even more, Dumfries has geographical possibilities as the regional growth centre of the South-West, in respect of population, market and social services, industrial pursuits and communications. The Cumnock-Sanquhar and Girvan areas, by attracting new industry, have also similar prospects for the future.

North East Scotland (the area between the Firths of Tay and Moray)

The Plan draws a contrast between the economic fortunes of the Dundee and Aberdeen areas.

Dundee has been fortunate in ensuring its future security by the development of a wide range of industrial activities. The largest source of employment is still the jute industry, but the new industries have now achieved a growth sufficient to offset reverses in its traditional pursuits. Dundee is regarded in the Plan as a major focus of expansion. It derives some benefit from the fact that, locationally, it is not estranged from the industrial sphere of the Central Lowlands, an advantage which is now enhanced by

---

in population expected. New industry required. (2) Dundee area (43 per cent of population). Slight increase in population expected. Dundee a major focus for expansion.

Smaller towns with scope for development; burghs with population over 3,000 located along trunk routes.

The Borders: The area most seriously affected by depopulation. Four-fifths live in middle and lower Tweed valley. Berwick on Tweed is most suited to attract people and industry in eastern area. Galashiels: selected in the Plan for rapid expansion. 25,000 more people required in ten to fifteen years.

South West: Increasing unemployment, especially in the west. (1) Cumnock-Sanquhar area and (2) Dumfries-Annan area hold the best prospects for the future.

improved communications. Furthermore, the Plan predicts that, were the population of Dundee to increase to a quarter of a million, the city could become one of the strongest regional centres of Scotland. In the long term, the stability of the city will be translated to the smaller townships of the entire area from north Fife, along the Angus coast as far as Arbroath and Montrose, as well as inland to Perth and the smaller towns of Strathmore, like Forfar and Blairgowrie.

In contrast, Aberdeen seems to suffer in two respects. Territorially it is outwith the main industrial and mineral zone of Scotland. In addition, for many years, Aberdeen has experienced a regular drainage of workers from the city. Professional men as well as skilled mechanics and engineers leave to seek employment and advancement in other parts of Great Britain and overseas. Aberdeen is a strong regional centre and its industries are varied, but its post-war development has been slow. The Plan makes the point that 'the existing labour force in Aberdeen does not offer the same opportunity for rapid expansion as that in the Dundee area'. A programme of industrial development, with an attendant house building scheme, is prescribed as a necessity for a more prosperous city.

Similar treatment is advocated for the smaller townships that are situated along the north-east coastal fringe. Market towns and fishing ports like Fraserburgh, Peterhead, Banff, Macduff, Huntly, Keith, Buckie and Elgin, are encouraged to become small industrial growth centres, engaged in industry on a modest scale, and dependent on a local supply of labour. Already, within the last decade, there have been signs in this north-eastern corner of the commencements of new pursuits, or the expansion of older activities.

The Highlands and Islands (*The Crofting Counties together with some adjoining areas*).

Less need be said of the forecasts for this region, since the Plan follows most of the lines laid down in the previous Report (see pp. 248-252). Natural resources, on which are based the assets of forestry, tourism, and a special type of manufacturing industry, are set against the decline in the primary industries of agriculture and fishing (which has led to decay in remote areas, and demographic imbalance in the region generally). But new data has been used in foreseeing the possibilities of these assets being focused most advantageously in certain areas which have the soundest reserves of population, rather than being dispersed as 'pretexts for shoring up decaying communities'. (These foci are shown on the accompanying map.) Some guide lines are suggested, too, in the type of industry: the examples of existing successful enterprise are thought to have significance for other larger labour catchments, while in general the formula invoked is the obvious one of a 'high value to weight product'. It is suggested that planning should be phased, to some extent, especially in the need for some 'modest intermediate expansion' of manufacturing to hold the population until forestry and its attendant industries form a more enduring source of employment in many Highland areas.

*   *   *

This account of the Plan may fittingly terminate with a reference to the subsequent development at Dounreay (noted on p. 252), where, despite remoteness and sparse population, the Caithness area will gain a new assurance from the growth of a highly skilled technological labour force, and from the guarantee of power supplies to meet industrial needs in the future. This unique project puts Britain well ahead in the development of fast reactor plant, and it is the latest example of the striking series of changes and advances that will permeate all aspects of Scotland's economy.

INDEX